DATE DUE

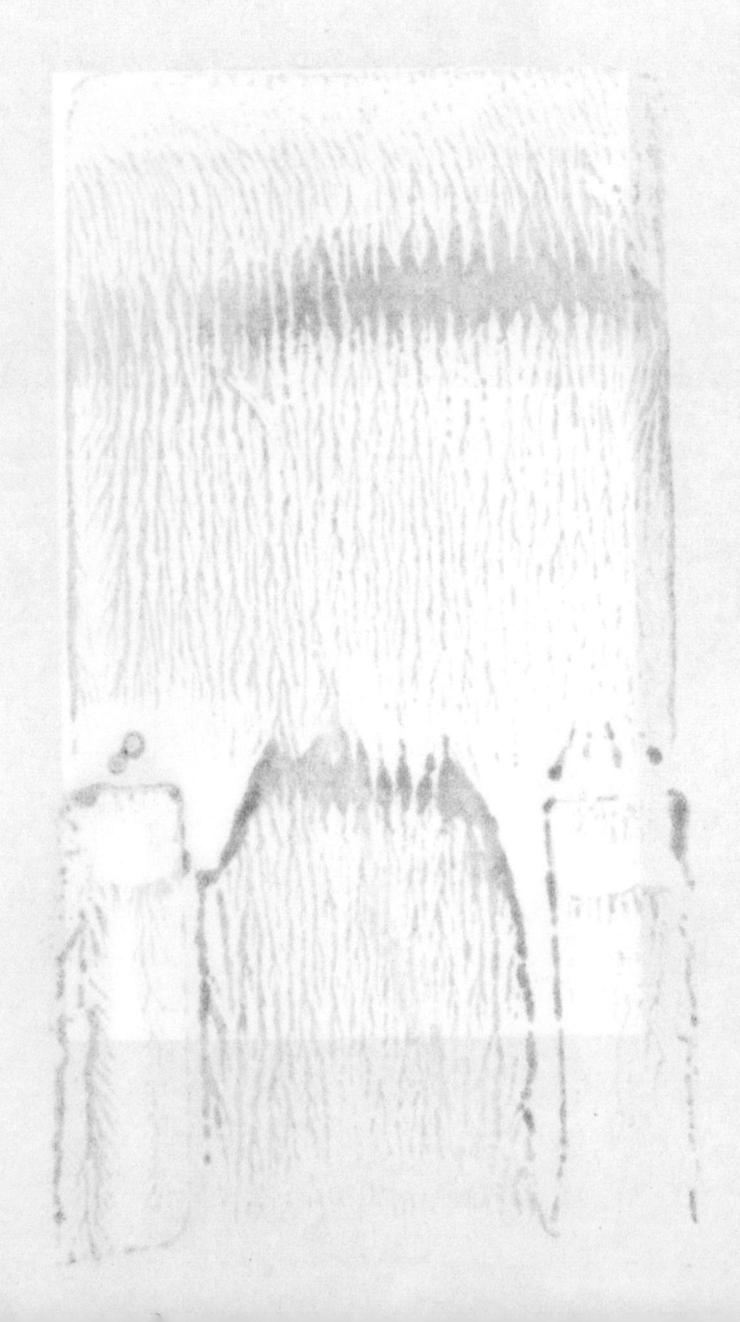

MONGOOSES

THEIR NATURAL HISTORY AND BEHAVIOUR

MONGOOSES

THEIR NATURAL HISTORY AND BEHAVIOUR

H. E. HINTON Sc.D., F.R.S.

A. M. S. DUNN M.A.

UNIVERSITY OF CALIFORNIA PRESS
BERKELEY AND LOS ANGELES · 1967

UNIVERSITY OF CALIFORNIA PRESS
BERKELEY AND LOS ANGELES, CALIFORNIA

Published in Great Britain by Oliver and Boyd Ltd.

Library of Congress Catalog
Card No. 67-28032

Printed in Great Britain

Preface

IN this book we have attempted to provide the most complete account of the natural history and behaviour of mongooses that has yet appeared: that we have missed some papers that we ought to have seen is certain, but we hope that time will show that there are relatively few of these.

A book is never finished, but there comes a time when it is abandoned and some matters left unsettled. A few points that we have failed to clear up may be briefly mentioned. There are no poisonous snakes in Jamaica, but a number of writers say that at one time the fer-de-lance was introduced into the island in order to frighten slaves from trying to escape at night. It is also sometimes said that vipers were introduced into the islands of St Lucia and Martinique for the same purpose. We have discovered no documents that would support such stories: poisonous snakes might bite the slave-owners. In 1966 it was widely reported in the press that a mongoose had been introduced into Italy for an experiment in the control of vipers, but we know nothing about the outcome of the experiment. A species of mongoose, possibly the Indian mongoose, has been introduced into some of the Fiji islands. Unfortunately we have been unable to learn from the Department of Agriculture at Suva either its name or its economic status.

Dr R. F. Ewer assisted in many ways: in particular she gave us permission to reproduce line drawings from her papers, and she gave us a number of previously unpublished photographs of the meerkat, which we have been glad to use. Dr G. Dücker gave us permission to reproduce some of her illustrations and also gave us a complete set of her papers on mongooses. We are very grateful to Dr Gouri Ganguly for her translations from one of the editions of the *Panchatantra* and for the other Indian stories reproduced in Chapter XII.

Mr R. W. Hayman of the British Museum (Natural History) gave us much help with the taxonomy of mongooses. Dr I. E. S. Edwards of the Department of Egyptian Antiquities of the British

Museum provided references to some of the important work on the mongoose in ancient Egypt.

We are also grateful to the following: Mrs Joyce Ablett for assistance in searching the literature, Dr George Cansdale for some of his personal observations on mongooses, Professor D. W. Ewer for a list of the local names of mongooses in Ghana, Mr E. O. Pearson for his assistance in finding some of the more obscure papers on mongooses, Dr C. David Simpson for photographs of the banded mongoose, Mr K. D. Taylor of the Infestation Control Division of the Ministry of Agriculture for some of the literature on the mongoose in the West Indies, and to Dr C. B. Williams, F.R.S., for lending us some rare works on the mongoose in the West Indies.

Miss E. C. Leschke and Miss G. Wigge saved us much time by translating some of the more difficult German papers.

H. E. Hinton
A. M. S. Dunn

Bristol
January 1967

Contents

I

General natural history

ALMOST all types of country are inhabited by one or another species of mongoose: *Cynictis* and the meerkat may colonise dry and sandy plains with little vegetation other than low grass; *Atilax* lives beside permanent bodies of water and often in marshes, as does *Herpestes urva*; other kinds live in open forest country; and still others live in the thick jungle and rarely venture into open country. Some species, such as *Herpestes sanguineus*, inhabit a very wide variety of environments: arid hills on which there is only a little stunted vegetation, or thick scrub or low forest, or level sandy plains whether comparatively open, bush-covered, or lightly wooded.

Mongooses are essentially terrestrial. Nearly all species are very poor tree-climbers and are rarely seen on anything but the lowest branches. However, *Herpestes sanguineus* is exceptional, and its climbing ability is said to resemble that of a squirrel (Shortridge, 1934). Well-adapted arboreal animals, like most of the Viverrinae, will climb down tree-trunks, branches, and other objects head first, but animals poorly adapted for climbing usually climb down backwards. *Herpestes sanguineus* is unusual in that it climbs down forwards, and we have often seen *H. edwardsi* climb down wire netting and low trees, head first.

All species swim well when forced to do so, and a few species are semi-aquatic or aquatic such as *Atilax* in Africa, *Herpestes urva* and *H. vitticollis* in India, and *H. brachyurus* in the East Indies. These species subsist largely on fresh-water crabs, frogs, and fish. The most aquatic of them is certainly *Atilax*, which dives and swims somewhat like an otter. When it is pursued it may remain for long periods completely submerged with only its nose sticking above the surface.

They generally live in cavities among the roots of trees, in shelters among rocks, or in the abandoned burrows of other animals such as ground squirrels, rabbits, porcupines, and aardvarks. Some such as *Suricata* and *Cynictis* may either dig their own burrows or use those of ground squirrels. Most species live singly or in pairs, or, when their offspring are young, in small family parties. A number of species, however, are gregarious and live in small to large communities, e.g. *Suricata*, *Cynictis*, and *Mungos*.

Most kinds of mongooses are diurnal and emerge from their sleeping places well after sunrise. Some species are both diurnal and nocturnal, e.g. *H. ichneumon* (Flower, 1932; Roberts, 1951; Shortridge, 1934), *H. fuscus* (Webb-Peploe, 1947), and *H. vitticollis* (Kinloch, 1923; Prater, 1935). *Ichneumia* is usually strictly nocturnal (Maberly, 1960), but in secluded places it will sometimes hunt in the afternoon (Fitzsimons, 1919). *Atilax* is also essentially nocturnal and seldom seen by day (Shortridge, 1934). Some species that hunt chiefly by day will hunt by night when there is a moon and the weather is warm, e.g. *H. sanguineus*. Other species that will normally hunt by day in the wilder parts of their range tend to hunt by night in the more populated parts, e.g. *H. fuscus* (Phillips, 1925).

FOOD

Like most Viverridae, mongooses are omnivorous carnivores. The nature of their food depends to a large extent on the opportunities offered by the localities in which they find themselves. Probably the bulk of the food taken by most species in their natural environment consists of insects and spiders, but when opportunity offers they eat snails, slugs, frogs, toads, lizards, snakes, birds, eggs of reptiles and birds, all kinds of rodents such as mice, rats, rock dassies and other mammals up to the size of hares. Species that normally feed on insects, amphibia, reptiles, birds, and rodents may subsist largely on crabs and fish. For instance, the small Indian mongoose feeds largely on crabs and fish caught in shallow intertidal pools in some places in Hawaii (Fig. 1).

Many species will eat fruits, berries, nuts, roots and tubers, and young leaves. Tame meerkats will eat tomatoes, pears, bananas, green peas, carrots, and avocado pears were a favourite food. Complaints have been made in Ohau that the small Indian mongoose injured bananas. This mongoose would eat ripe bananas, especially their skins, when more acceptable food was not available (Pemberton, 1933). It was especially fond of papayas (Walker, 1945). A pet banded mongoose developed a strong liking for salad but only if this was liberally mixed with French dressing (Kinloch,

1964). Some species such as *H. edwardsi* will eat carrion, and this species has often been seen feeding on the abandoned kills of the larger carnivora (Prater, 1935). *H. vitticollis* (Fernando, 1913) and other species are attracted to dead fish.

In one area of Ceylon, *Herpestes smithi* is said to feed chiefly on the large snail, *Achatina* (Phillips, 1925). In Africa *Atilax* is said to be, with the monitor lizard, one of the most important enemies of the crocodile, scratching out from the sand and eating the eggs whenever it can (Stevenson-Hamilton, 1947). The ancient Romans (e.g. Diodorus, 1, 35, 7) affirmed that the Egyptian ichneumon broke the eggs of the crocodile, not for the sake of food, but from a benevolent motive towards mankind, whose welfare it sought to promote by killing the offspring of that odious animal. 'Were it not for the service it thus renders to the country, the river would become unapproachable, from the multitude of crocodiles; and it even kills them when full-grown, by means of a wonderful and almost incredible contrivance. Covering itself with a coat of mud, the ichneumon watches the moment when the crocodile, coming out of the river, sleeps (as is its custom) upon a sand bank, with its mouth open (turned towards the wind), and, adroitly gliding down its throat, penetrates to its entrails. It then gnaws through its stomach, and, having killed its enemy, escapes without receiving any injury.'

Fig. 1. *Herpestes urva*, the crab-eating mongoose. The hind legs of the crab are missing. (Based on Lydekker)

The most complete study of the amount of food eaten by a mongoose in the field is that of Williams (1918) for the small Indian mongoose, *H. auropunctatus*, on the island of Trinidad. From an examination of the stomachs of 180 individuals, Williams estimated the quantity and kind of food that might be taken by a single mongoose over a period of three months. The injurious animals in the following list are indicated by an asterisk.

Total food of a mongoose for three months

Vertebrates	*	common rat	26
	*	spiney rat	2
		miscellaneous birds	14
		domestic fowl	10
		fowl eggs	2
		lizards	17
		snakes	18
		frogs	15
		toads	14
		fish	6
Insects	*	grasshoppers	535
	*	mole crickets	2
	*	crickets	3
		cockroaches	54
	*	stick insect	1
	*	moths	3
	*	caterpillars	2
		fly larvae	27
	*	plant bugs	2
	*	scarabaeid beetles	43
	*	scarabaeid larvae	7
	*	carabid larvae	44
	*	weevils	7
	*	weevil larvae	7
		miscellaneous beetles	46
		ants	3
Other arthropods		spiders	44
		scorpion	1
		centipedes	14
		millipede	1
		tick	1
	*	crab	3
Vegetable matter		fruits	6
		yam	one feed
		coconut	a little

Herpestes, *Atilax*, *Mungos*, *Helogale*, and possibly all Herpestini deal with hard-shelled objects such as eggs, snails, mussels, crabs,

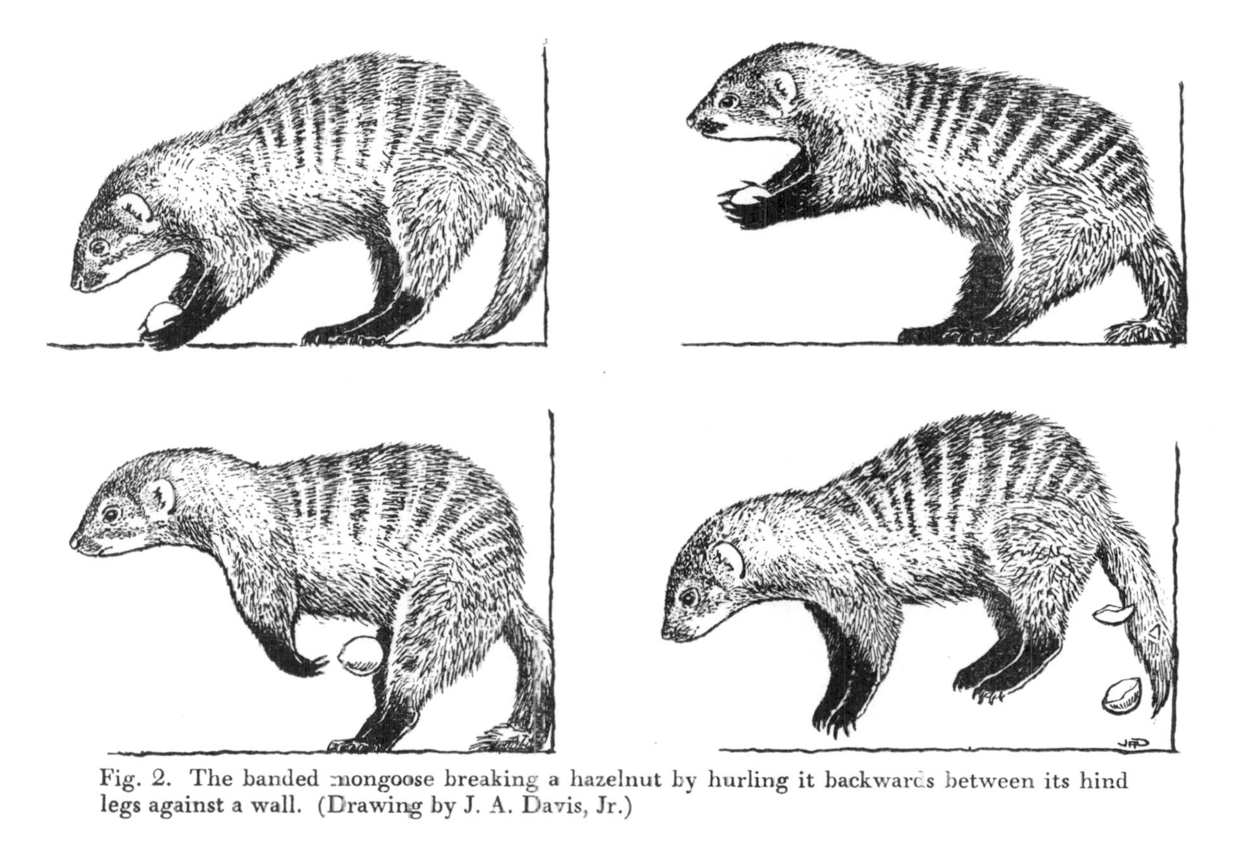

Fig. 2. The banded mongoose breaking a hazelnut by hurling it backwards between its hind legs against a wall. (Drawing by J. A. Davis, Jr.)

nuts, and so on in one of two very characteristic ways.† The mongoose may pick up the object to be broken between its front paws, stand on its hind legs, and hurl it violently down on the ground. Or it may throw it backwards between its hind legs against a wall, or rock, or other solid vertical face (Fig. 2). In preparation for the backward throw, it may roll the object close to the nearest wall or pick it up between its front paws and clutching it to its chest stand on its hind legs and waddle close to the wall. It then suddenly turns its back to the wall, spreads its hind legs, and flings the object between its hind legs against the wall. It then springs around and, if the object has been broken sufficiently, sets about eating it. If the object has not been broken, the manoeuvre is repeated. It may be repeated again and again if the object is very hard. Loveridge (pp. 82-83) described the behaviour of banded mongooses with cockle shells which they were unable to smash, as follows: 'Instead of being discouraged, the futility of their efforts served only to increase their eagerness, which became almost unbalanced in the intensity with which they vied with each other in violent attempts to smash the mollusc. Between times they would fight desperately for possession of the shell, though often, after gaining it, the possessor would fear to fling it lest his waiting relative should filch it. This distrust led to much waddling about for position.' Kinloch (p. 78) says of an individual of the same species for which a supply of shells was kept in the house: '. . . it became a common sight to see him practising his throwing technique at almost any hour of the day . . . virtually any object would do for throwing practice . . . A bunch of keys in the bedroom, hurled repeatedly against Elizabeth's back or legs as she lay resting; a wine cork against my knees; an empty medicine tube against the cushions of the settee.' Brownlow found that a crab-eating mongoose would employ a stone or golf ball in a similar manner. At the time of impact the mongoose would jump clear to avoid its legs being hit. Brownlow found that the force used when it was playing this game against a hard surface was sufficient to bruise his shin severely.

The banded mongoose and some species of *Herpestes* may at different times use either the vertical or the backward throw to

†Brownlow (1940b), Cansdale (1946), Davis (1966), Dücker (1957, 1965), Grote (1909), Kinloch (1964), Lombard (1958), Loveridge (1944), Matschie (1895), Morris (1961), Nordmann (1863), Pitman (1954), Pocock (1941), Prater (1948), Sclater (1900), Simpson (1964, 1966), Steinbacher (1939, 1951), Walker (1948).

Plate I. The Indian mongoose biting a dead bird offered to it.

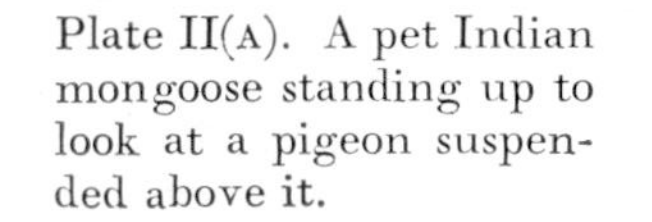

Plate II(A). A pet Indian mongoose standing up to look at a pigeon suspended above it.

Plate II(B). The banded mongoose.

break hard objects. Both methods of throwing often become part of their play ritual. Both methods are innate. For instance, the backward throw was practised by a young *Atilax* that had been reared by hand and had no opportunity to learn it (Cansdale, 1946). Neither method of breaking hard objects has been observed in the meerkat, although probably most is known about the behaviour of this species. Sterndale (1884) found that *H. edwardsi* dealt with eggs in quite a different way: it would hold them in its front paws and crack a little hole at the small end out of which it would suck the contents.

HUNTING AND CAPTURE OF PREY

Most species of mongooses have been seen hunting singly, in pairs, or in small family parties. Some are usually seen hunting alone. For instance, Stoner (1944) says that the striped-necked mongoose always hunts alone, but others have seen it hunting in pairs. According to Wroughton (1915), the natives of Ceylon say that when it hunts it is accompanied by *H. smithi* and *H. fuscus* which warn it of any danger, a story that is hardly worth investigating. A few species hunt in large groups, e.g. *Helogale parvula* in groups of up to 15 and *Mungos mungo* in packs of 10 to 20 and very occasionally up to 100, and *Crossarchus obscurus* in packs (Drake-Brockman, 1910; Heller, 1911; Hollister, 1918; Simpson, 1964). The meerkat and *Cynictis* live in communities in burrows, sometimes in fairly large groups, up to 50 individuals of *Cynictis* being found in a single colony.

Not enough is known about the behaviour of mongooses in the field to say to what extent they co-operate when tackling larger animals or dangerous ones like poisonous snakes. It seems probable that co-operation of this kind is common, at least among the more social species. Aristotle said that when the ichneumon saw a snake it did not attack it until it had called upon other ichneumons for help. Two or more individuals of the dwarf mongoose, *Helogale parvula*, will co-operate in attacking snakes (Sclater, 1900; Stevenson-Hamilton, 1947). Simpson (1964) observed a pack of about ten banded mongooses killing a large sand snake. La Rivers (1948) observed two individuals of *Herpestes auropunctatus* working together looking for shore crabs, *Metopograspus messor*. One turned over the stones and the other pounced upon the crab flushed from beneath, whereupon both consumed part of the crab and then resumed their hunt for more. It is said that whereas the Hawaiian goose can protect its young from a single mongoose, two or more can sufficiently distract the goose so that they can take its young (Shipman *in* Baldwin, 1952). Two individuals of *Herpestes fuscus* removed marral over 21 pounds in weight from a water hole at night. It is believed that this was done by one of them entering the pool and driving the fish shorewards while the other lay in wait (Hutton, 1949).

The manner in which the mongoose deals with snakes and other venomous animals is treated in the chapter that follows. We are now concerned only to summarise a few miscellaneous observations that have been made on the way prey is caught and on unusual kinds of prey.

Hardly any attention has been paid to the way in which mongooses lure certain kinds of prey by exciting their curiosity with unusual antics, although much has been written on this subject for other groups of carnivores. On moonlight nights the white-tailed mongoose, *Ichneumia*, was sometimes seen to dance outside the wire netting of poultry pens (Pitman, 1954). This excited the curiosity of the fowls, which sometimes stuck their heads out through the wire netting only to have them bitten off promptly. In Zambia a mongoose (*Mungos* ?) was seen to stand on its hind legs and then fall sideways, first on one side and then on the other. An inquisitive flock of guinea fowl drew gradually closer to observe the animal, whereupon it suddenly sprang among them and killed four (Preston, 1950).

Although the chief use that has been made of mongooses is as rat-catchers, it is their ability to deal with snakes that has everywhere caught popular imagination. In all the countries they inhabit they are to a greater or lesser extent used as rat-catchers in houses; and in the not so distant past both *H. edwardsi* and *H. auropunctatus* were often kept as pets on ships to help rid them of rats.

Even the largest rats are unable effectively to defend themselves against a mongoose, which is not only bigger but is also very much more agile. Fights between rats and the small Indian mongoose are gruesomely described by Dotty (1945, p. 83): 'While these wild mongooses were shy, they were savage and would "spit" vigorously whenever an observer drew close to the cage, and were always over-anxious to get at the rat as it was being transferred to their cage. Each time a rat was being transferred to one of the mongoose's cages, that mongoose would reach through the cage door and seize the rat before it could even be hurriedly thrust through the opening. The most agile rat seemed to have no chance to even put up a fight with the mongoose. In a flash and unerringly, the mongoose always grabbed the rat by the back of the neck on the first pass and, while growling like a cat with a mouthful of mouse and with his long sharp teeth pierced through the neck, would begin to crush the rat's bones. The cracking of the bones during this fiasco fight was plainly audible to the observer. The initial struggling of the rat generally ceased in less than 30 seconds. When the rat became limp, the mongoose would put it down and then take a few more savage bites around the rat's head to make a finished job of the killing. In a few minutes the mongoose would start eating the rat, beginning at the head. He would leisurely yet completely consume the rat including the viscera leaving, as the only evidence of a hearty meal, a part of the tail and perhaps a foot or two and a small strip of skin with hair.'

An account of how the Indian mongoose forces a hedgehog to unroll and then kills it is given by O'Brien (1919). In the West Indies the small Indian mongoose attacks and kills fawns of the white-tailed deer several times its own weight (Seaman & Randall, 1962), and in Mauritius the Indian mongoose is partly responsible for the near extinction of Sambar deer (Maingard, 1954). Lewis (1940) records an incident in which a large grey mongoose (*H. edwardsi* ?) seized a donkey by the snout and would not let go until it received a tap on the back from the butt end of a gun. It seems probable that the donkey was attacked because it accidentally stepped on or very near the mongoose: it is hardly likely that any mongoose would attempt to kill so large an animal.

ENEMIES

In Chapter XVI an account is given of the diseases and parasites of mongooses. Besides these, the larger carnivora attack them, and probably birds of prey account for numbers of those, such as the meerkat and the yellow mongoose, that live in more open country.

Man and his dogs are probably among their chief enemies in most areas. The small Indian mongoose is poisoned on a massive scale in both the Hawaiian Islands and in the West Indies, and probably a good proportion of men with a gun will shoot a mongoose when they see one. In Kashmir a game act classified mongooses as vermin and offered a reward for each killed (Singh, 1956). In many parts of Africa they are eaten by the local people. For instance, in

Northern Nigeria the hunters eat the dwarf mongoose despite the unpleasant odour that it has (Dr S. Toye, personal communication). The Chinese in Hawaii are said to eat them, and *Herpestes urva* is still imported into Hong Kong for food (Marshall & Phillips, 1965). Cansdale (1952) notes that the dwarf mongoose and the hyaena were the only two animals that were never eaten by others after they were skinned.

Accounts of dogs attacking mongooses are given by Adams (1931) and Fleur-de-Lys (1908). The striped-necked mongoose, *Herpestes vitticollis*, is well known for the readiness with which it will use the offensive secretion of its anal glands as a defensive fluid which it squirts at its enemies. Adams says that three dogs that killed an old male reeked of the musky odour for some time even though they had rolled in water.

Mongooses in the field are often mobbed by birds. According to Lister (1951), the Indian mongoose in Bengal is most frequently mobbed by the common myna and the magpie robin. Kinloch (1964) records an instance of the banded mongoose being mobbed by scarlet-headed lovebirds and a grey African parrot.

II

Snakes and other venomous animals

BOTH in the Oriental Region and in Egypt the ability of mongooses to kill venomous snakes early attracted attention. Aristotle (*Hist. Anim.* 9, 6) says, 'The Egyptian ichneumon, when it sees the serpent called the asp, does not attack it until it has called in other ichneumons to help*; to meet the blows and bites of their enemy the assailants beplaster themselves with mud, by first soaking in the river and then rolling on the ground.' Speaking of the Egyptian asp or cobra (*Naja haje*) three and a half centuries later, Pliny the Elder (8, c. 35-36) says, 'It is impossible to declare whether Nature has engendered evils or remedies more bountifully. In the first place she has bestowed on this accursed creature dim eyes, and those not in the forehead for it to look straight in front of it, but in the temples . . .; and in the next place she has given it war to the death with the ichneumon . . . The ichneumon repeatedly plunges into mud and dries itself in the sun, and then when it has equipped itself with a cuirass of several coatings by the same method, it proceeds to the encounter. In this it raises its tail and renders the blows it receives ineffectual by turning away from them, till after watching for its opportunity, with head held sideways it attacks its adversary's throat. And not content with this victim it vanquishes another animal no less ferocious, the crocodile.'

Strabo (17, 1, 39) said that the ichneumon killed the asp by seizing it by the tail or head and dragging it into the river. Aelian (*Nat. Anim.* 3, 22) embellished the accounts of Aristotle and Pliny. According to him, if no mud was near the ichneumon rolled itself in the sand. Its nose, which alone remained exposed, was then enveloped in several folds of its tail, and it thus commenced its attack. If bitten, its death was inevitable; but all efforts of the asp were unavailing against its artificial coat of mail, and the ichneu-

* The statement that several ichneumons help each other in killing the asp is incorrectly attributed to Pliny by Wilkinson (1878).

mon, attacking it on a sudden, seized it by the throat and immediately killed it. Topsell writing in the sixteenth century says, '... when the aspe espyth her threatening rage, presently turning about her taile, provoketh the ichneumon to combate and with an open mouth and lofty head doth enter the list, to her own perdition. For the ichneumon being nothing afraid of this great bravado, receiveth the encounter, and taking the head of the aspe in his mouth biteth that off to prevent the casting out of her poison.'

Fights between mongooses and cobras have been photographed and filmed on a number of occasions. Examination of the photographs leaves little room to doubt the course of events. Particularly good accounts have been given by Buytendijk (1932) and Deraniyagala (1932). The latter staged a fight between the spectacled cobra or cobra-de-capello, *Naja naja*, and *Herpestes edwardsi*. The cobra was 6 ft. 3 in. long and the mongoose 16 in. long. Deraniyagala's account, save for the addition of a few punctuation marks, is as follows:

'The cobra was the first to be liberated into the wire-netted enclosure. It took up a central position, coiled itself, and regarded the onlookers with raised hood, which it elevated to nearly double the previous height on seeing the mongoose. From this height of about 50 centimetres it lashed out savagely whenever the latter came within range but was too slow to land.

'For fifteen minutes the mongoose, worried by its unusual surrounding, attempted to escape and completely ignored the presence of the cobra. After a short rest it resumed its exertions, but suddenly uttering its short strident cry it walked up to the cobra with tail bristling. For a second they faced each other, and, as the snake which towered above the mongoose opened its jaws and drew back its hood to strike, the mongoose darted in and sprang for the lower jaw, simultaneously gripping the cobra's body with all four legs as it bit. The snake shot up in a writhing mass of coils taking the mongoose aloft with it, then both fell to the ground where, as they struggled body to body, the latter worked its jaws with a crunching action, its snout always keeping contact with the snake. Once an effective grip was obtained, the mongoose was content to slacken its body and was not particular whether it was swung off its feet on to its back or constricted in the coils of the snake. Finally the mongoose twisted over on to its back in order to render its bite more damaging.

'The entire struggle lasted about five seconds after which the mongoose broke loose and resumed its attempts to escape. This may have been due to the buzz of conversation of the onlookers scaring it, or it may be that the animal normally fights in short sharp bursts as is said to be its mode of combat according to those who have seen such fights in the jungle.

'The cobra was crippled by the bites and could not raise itself to its former height, and its lower jaw hung broken on the right side. From time to time the mongoose attacked the cobra, which during the interval early in the fight lowered its hood and attempted to escape. This was the only attempt at flight, and thereafter it remained game. In attack the mongoose invariably went for the snout, jaws, or cheeks, usually seizing the cobra as it gaped prior to striking. By seizing the snake in this manner it will be noticed that the jaws of the mongoose would come between those of the snake, and such appeared to be the case. Early in the fight the mongoose attacked with a quick rush from the side, but once it had slowed the cobra down it sprang straight in regardless of danger. The cobra's bites may not have been without effect, for often after a round the mongoose slaked its thirst at the pond within the enclosure. It is also probable that thirst was induced merely by its exertions, for once warmed up it manifested a total disregard of the cobra's bites and often remained within striking distance with its back to the foe.

'A conspicuous feature was that once the cobra raised the fore part of its body, it struck with this length fully extended and was unable to shorten up. The mongoose was comparatively safe when it sprang past this striking circle into close quarters, as it did time and again. When close to the snake it waited at times for as long as eight seconds until the dazed cobra opened its jaws to strike, when it would spring up, seize a jaw, pull the cobra down, and worry it. Throughout the fight the mongoose ignored the snake's body and attacked the head, sometimes shifting its grip on to the upper part of the hood during the struggle.

'The cobra was very exhausted and missed the mongoose by wider and wider margins and gasped for breath with open jaws, the glottis protruding as a round, tubate opening. The mongoose was also very tired, and it panted hard with open jaws as it ran around the enclosure seeking to escape, while the ferocity of its onslaught had abated considerably. Although it had almost run itself to a standstill, time and again it would deliberately walk up to the snake, raise itself on its hind legs and fasten on to the cobra's jaw as it gaped to strike. However, it could no longer maintain its grip as it had to relax its hold to pant.

'At this stage the fight was stopped after it had progressed for fifty minutes. Had it continued, the cobra would have been killed. Examination of the mongoose revealed two gashes in its upper lip, and it is very probable that these were fang marks. The animal was immediately placed in a concrete floored cage and showed no ill effects whatsoever.'

The cobra had a fractured jaw, but in due course it recovered. The essential features of the fight were: (1) The mongoose never attacked the cobra's body; (2) it sprang inside the cobra's striking circle and awaited the attack at close quarters; (3) once warmed up, the mongoose did not avoid the cobra's bite as it sprang in; (4) the mongoose fought in rounds lasting about five seconds each; (5) after most rounds it drank water; (6) once on the ground, both animals rolled over and over, the cobra at times constricting the mongoose which turned over on to its back; (7) the striking radius of the cobra depended upon the length of body it erected, and when the mongoose was within this radius it was comparatively safe; (8) the cobra was comparatively slow in striking; and (9) there were no rents in the skin of the cobra although there were numerous punctures.

There are many accounts of more or less staged fights between mongooses and poisonous snakes, chiefly cobras.* Almost without exception writers emphasise the point that it is the speed and agility of the mongoose that is chiefly responsible for its success. When the mongoose is fighting, its hair is erected so that it often appears twice its natural size (Plate III, opposite), and, as Prater and others point out, this must often cause the snake to strike short.

The cobra's fangs are in the front of the upper jaw and are immovable and relatively short. The cobra has to bite and chew or scratch. Its mouth is only opened to about 45 degrees when striking. Thus neither in its method of striking nor in the structure of its fangs is the cobra adapted for quick injection of its venom. In defence the cobra has the anterior one-sixth to one-third of the body raised vertically. From this position it strikes forwards and

* Anonymous (1936), Beddard (1909), Blanford (1888), Buytendijk (1932, 1952), Calmette (1898), Deraniyagala (1951), Fayrer (1872), Kipling (1891), Lewis (1913), Oliver (1955), Pergus (1852), Phillips (1935), Pocock (1941), Prater (1935, 1948), Roosevelt (1910), Sterndale (1884), Stevenson-Hamilton (1947).

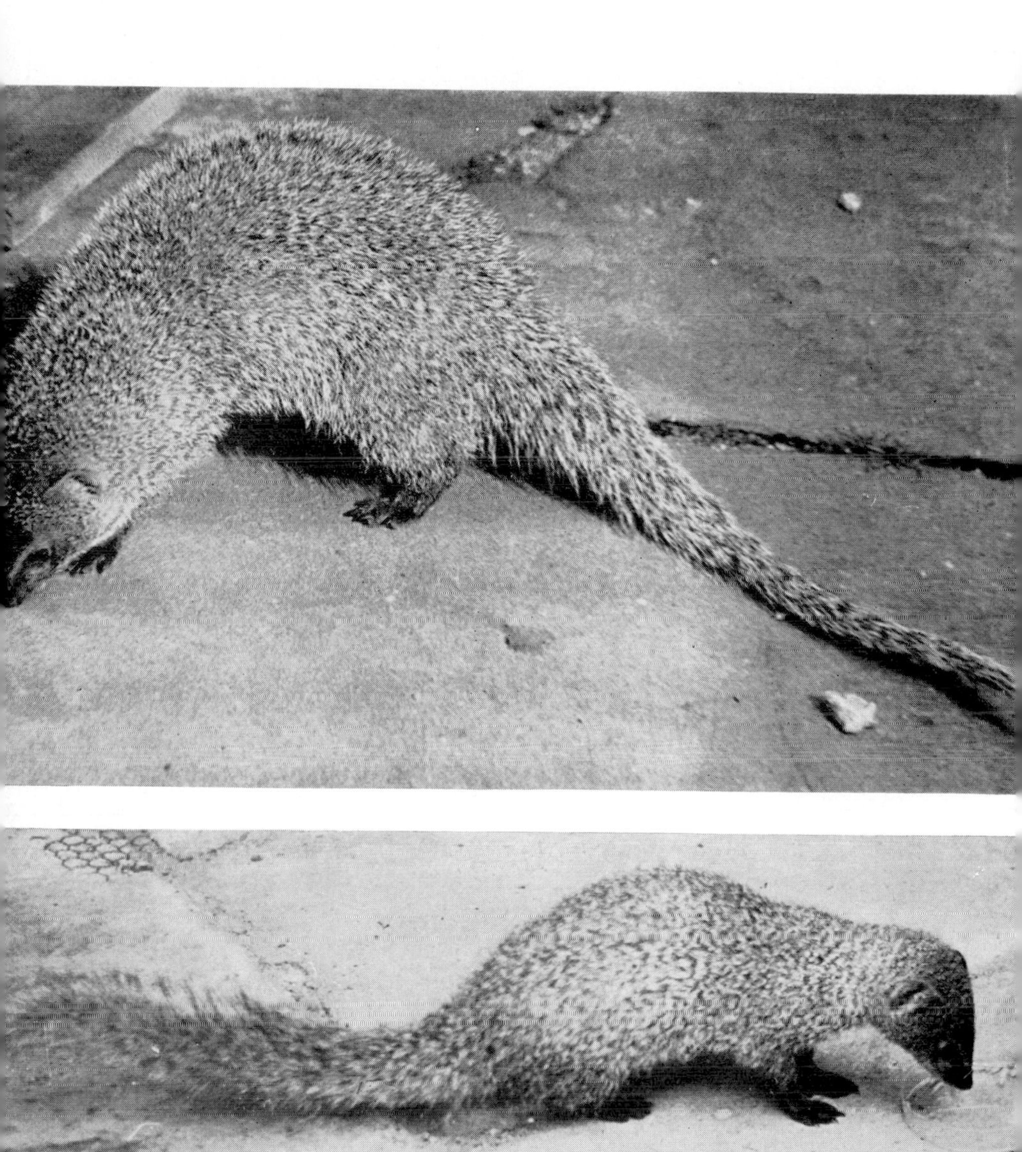

Plate III. A pet Indian mongoose. In the upper photograph the hairs of the body are partly erected but those of the tail are not. In the lower photograph only the hairs of the tail are erected.

Plate IV(A). A young meerkat drinking milk out of a saucer.

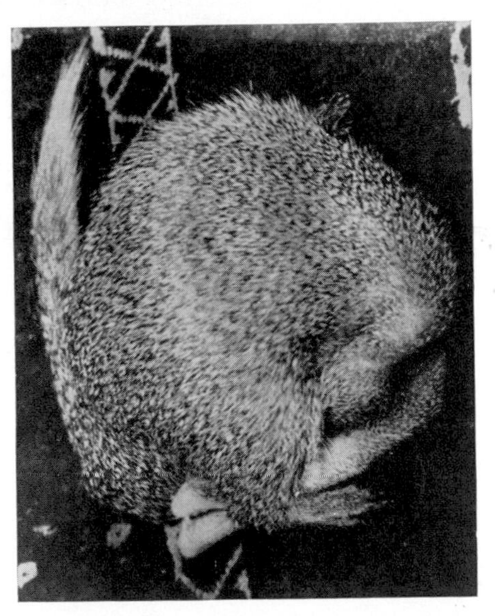

Plate IV(B). Special ultimate defence posture of the Indian mongoose, *Herpestes edwardsi*. (After Rensch and Dücker)

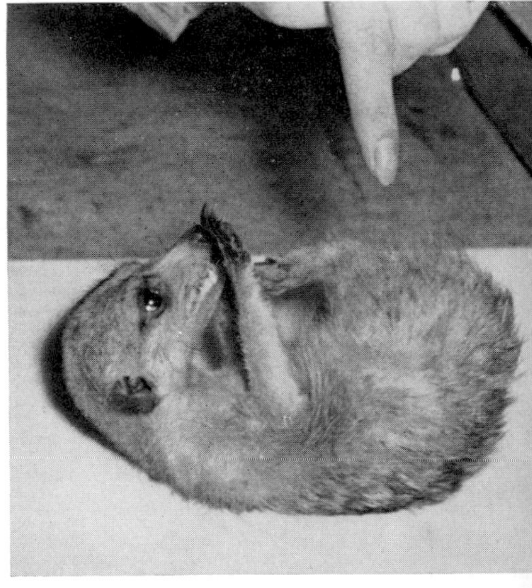

Plate IV(C). A meerkat showing the ultimate defence posture of mongooses and carnivores in general. In this position the vulnerable nape of the neck is protected and the claws and teeth are directed towards the aggressor. (After Dücker)

downwards for a distance a little more than the raised part of its body. It is relatively slow: its strike is only about a sixth as fast as that of a rattlesnake (Oliver, 1955). A normally active mongoose can thus sidestep the strike of a cobra and has many chances to bite it in the neck or head.

Vipers of comparable size may be much more effective against mongooses. Their fangs lie along the roof of the mouth. When about to strike they open their mouth some 180 degrees and raise their fangs about 90 degrees. In the act of striking they are actually leading with the tips of the fangs. As a rule, the front part of the body is drawn into an S-shaped loop. In a strike the head is thrust forwards with considerable speed and force. We are unable to find any report of a mongoose naturally attacking a large viper. Remains of a rhinoceros viper have been found in the stomach of a wild *Bdeogale* (Beddard, 1909). In the West Indies there are two pit vipers, the fer-de-lance and the bushmaster, but there appear to be no authentic reports of either of these vipers in the very numerous mongoose stomachs examined by various people. Fights staged in the West Indies between the small Indian mongoose and pit vipers more often than not end in the victory of the viper. In a film made some years ago of a fight between a diamond-back rattlesnake and a mongoose, the mongoose emerged victorious, but two obviously different mongooses had taken part in the fight (Oliver, 1955).

Different kinds of mongooses behave differently towards snakes. In India where mongooses and cobras occur together they generally ignore each other. In Ceylon Phillips (1925) points out that the mongoose (*H. edwardsi lanka*) will not normally tackle a large snake. Cansdale (personal communication) says that his pet kusimanse was afraid of even a dead snake, and Loveridge (1944) says that the banded mongoose would treat even such harmless species as the brown house snake with great respect. When one was liberated in the open, the mongoose would run after it, bite its tail, and then spring back before the snake had time to strike.

We do not know whether snakes form any considerable part of the normal diet of any species of mongoose. Accounts of wild mongooses attacking wild snakes are, as might be expected, very uncommon, but this of itself does not prove anything. Smith (1914) came upon a fight between a four foot cobra (*Naja naja*) and *H. edwardsi* in which the mongoose killed the snake by biting it on the head. Also in India Foottit (1929) saw a species of mongoose kill an unidentified species of snake. The small Indian mongoose was introduced into Martinique and St Lucia to control the fer-de-lance, *Bothrops atrox* (Myers, 1931a, b). Although the viper is now very rare in Martinique and uncommon in St Lucia, it is by no means certain that the mongoose has had much to do with this decrease in its numbers.

There is quite good evidence that snakes are an unimportant part of the diet of the small Indian mongoose in the Caribbean Islands. Williams (1918) examined the stomachs of 180 mongooses of which 14 were empty. Each of 18 of the remaining 166 stomachs contained the remains of a small snake. All of the snakes that could be identified were harmless species. Snakes were present in only 4 of the 149 stomachs of mongooses killed and examined in Trinidad by Urich. In 59 stomachs examined in Puerto Rico, Wolcott (1953) found only two blind-snakes (*Typhlops lumbricalis*). The evidence from Trinidad is particularly significant: there are four venomous species on the island besides a number of harmless species.

Urich (1931) points out that in Trinidad the four kinds of poisonous snakes, two species of coral snakes and two pit vipers, have not been affected in any way by the mongoose (*H. auropunctatus*). The boas have held their own. *Corallus cooki*, the tree boa, is fairly common, and *Boa constrictor*, known as the macajuel, seems to be on the increase. Mongooses have been found in the stomachs of full grown individuals of the macajuel. Urich says: 'I have every reason to believe that this snake can exercise valuable control on the increase of the mongoose.' The Director of the Zoological Garden in Port-of-Spain feeds live, wild mongooses to his boas when other foods are scarce (Oliver, 1955). The common boa is said to feed extensively on the mongoose in St Lucia (Myers, 1931b).

RESISTANCE TO SNAKE VENOM

When animals of equal weights are compared it is found that some are more resistant to the venom of particular snakes than are others. In a general way, these differences in resistance seem to be related to their habits. The pig and the hedgehog are widely reputed to be more resistant to snake poisons than are other mammals. One of the favourite foods of the hedgehog is the viper. Phisalix & Bertrand found that to kill a hedgehog with the venom of *Vipera berus* they had to use 40 times the minimum lethal dose required to kill a guinea-pig.

Fayrer (1872) was perhaps the first clearly to demonstrate the fact that although the mongoose is not immune to cobra venom it is nevertheless less sensitive than other mammals. His conclusions were supported by the experiments of Calmette (1898, 1907; see also Noguchi, 1909). Calmette used the small Indian mongoose caught on the island of Guadeloupe where there are no poisonous snakes. The resistance of the mongoose to venom could not therefore have been due to their being accustomed to the bites of poisonous snakes. When a mongoose was inoculated with 1 milligramme of venom (*Naja naja*), which kills a 2-kg rabbit in 3 hours, it did not experience any discomfort although it was only about half as heavy as the rabbit. A mongoose given four times the lethal dose for the rabbit was not ill, but another given six times the lethal dose was uneasy for two days and then recovered. A third mongoose was given eight times the lethal dose for the rabbit, and it died in 12 hours. Doses of 2 to 7 ml of serum from mongooses that had never been bitten by snakes were injected into rabbits. When the rabbits were then inoculated with cobra venom all died, but they died much later than the control series that had not received the mongoose serum.

South African mongooses are generally highly resistant to the venom of the black mamba (Pitman, 1938). The median lethal dose for the mouse of venom from a number of kinds of cobras ranges from 0·5 to 0·75 milligrammes per kilogramme of mouse. Adjusting the figures given by Jsemonger (1962) we arrive at the following:

	Suricata suricatta (600 g)	mg/kg
Naja nivea Boie	lethal in 18 hours	33·3
Naja nivea	subcutaneous injection, recovered	16·6
	Herpestes pulverulentus (700 g)	
Naja nivea	lethal in 36 hours	28·5
Naja melanoleuca Hallow	recovered	21·8

In India there is a widespread belief that when bitten by a cobra the mongoose retires to the jungle to look for a plant known as Mungo root, *manquaswail*, or *mangus wail* (*Ophiorrhiza Mungos* L.) which it eats as an antidote to the venom (Blanford, 1888; Pocock, 1941; Prater, 1935). Some Africans believe that when *Helogale parvula* is bitten it also uses some antidote that preserves it from ill effects (Stevenson-Hamilton, 1947).

So fascinating an account of the use of simples by the mongoose as an antidote to snake venom has been given by Garcia da Orta (1563)* that we have felt compelled to reproduce it in large part:

'In the beautiful island of Ceylon, where there are many good fruits, forests and beasts for the chase, there are yet many of those serpents vulgarly called *cobras de capelo* . . . Against these God has given us this *pao de cobra*. It is found to be good against snake bites because in that island there are small beasts like ferrets (he means mongooses) which they call *quil*. They often fight with these serpents. When one of them knows that it must fight with them, or fears that it may be so, it bites off a piece of this root and rubs it, or rather anoints, with its paws which are wet with the juice. It puts this on the head and body, and the parts where it knows that the cobra will bite when it springs. It then fights with the cobra, biting and scratching until it is dead. If it does not succeed in killing the cobra, the snake having more force than its antagonist, the *quil* or *quirpele* rubs itself again with the root and returns to the combat, and at last conquers and kills its enemy. From this the Chingallas took an example, and saw that this root would be good against the bites of cobras. The Portuguese believed the good things that the natives said about the stick . . . To give you more faith in its credibility I will relate to you what this Franciscan Friar, who is worthy of belief, saw in Negapatam, which is on the mainland near Ceylon.

'Many Portuguese have these mungooses in their houses, tamed and domesticated, to kill the rats, and to fight the cobras de capello which the Yougues (Yogis) bring who seek for charity. These Yogues are Gentios who go about begging all over the country, sprinkled over with ashes, and are venerated by all the common people and by some Moors. Travelling over so many countries they know numerous medicines and modes of treatment, some true, others false. Some of the Yogues bring these cobras with their teeth drawn, for in that condition they can do no harm. By this means, and for the gain they make, they hold the cobras in their

* Da Orta was born at Elvas in 1490. He attended the Universities of Salamanca and Alcala de Henares. He was in India as a physician from 1534, much of the time in Goa where he died in 1564. His famous work was published on 10th April 1563 and was dedicated to the Count of Redondo who was the Portuguese Viceroy at the time. Da Orta's book was the third ever printed in India. The first was a Catechism (1557) by St Francis Xavier, the friend and disciple of Ignatius Loyala founder of the Society of Jesus. The second was the *Compendio espirituel* (1561) by the first Archbishop of Goa, Dr Pereira.

hands, put them round their necks and on their heads, and hold them to be enchanted, but I consider this to be a lie. It happened that a Portuguese in Negapatam sent to a Yogue to bring a cobra to have a fight with his mungoos. But the Yogue did not wish to do this because he had drawn several teeth of the cobra, in which its power lies. The mungoos, seeing that a fight was intended, first went under the seats to see if it could scent some stick or root of the *pao de cobra*. Not finding any it made itself wet with its own saliva, and came to fight with the cobra. The cobra darted at its head and wounded it badly two or three times, and the mungoos returned the blows with interest. They were parted, both being badly wounded, but the cobra worst. The Yogue, finding how the battle went, and that the cobra was alive, for it was healed afterwards, brought out another cobra whose teeth had not been drawn, and delivered it to the Portuguese who wanted to make the animals fight again. The Yogue had to stake most, as his cobra seemed to be dying, and he had to produce another. So the Portuguese gave him more than he had given him before, and the Yogue was satisfied. For his new cobra came better armed and the Portuguese, with his mungoos, got ready for the war. He brought the root and the mungoos bit it for some time, and then anointed itself with its paw, wetting it where it had been bitten. This it did on its head, loins, and stomach. The mungoos being prepared for the fray, the Yogue came with the serpent, which raised itself up nearly half its length and made a spring on the mungoos, wounding it on the body, then springing back it struck again, and so they went on, sometimes the cobra striking the mungoos, at others the mungoos biting the cobra. Finally the mungoos jumped at the cobra's head biting a little further back, and tore the cobra so that, being tired, it was killed, and the Yogue made desperate.'

Bromlow (1940a) found that some Burmans believe that the mongoose has a patch on its tongue that contains medicine to counteract the bite of a poisonous snake. There is a patch of horny papillae on the tongue of a mongoose. These papillae, however, function as a rasp in removing flesh adhering to bones, and similar papillae are present on the tongues of many Carnivora.

TOADS

All toads have large poison glands, and it is sometimes suggested that for this reason they are unacceptable to mongooses. For instance, Seaman (1952) says that it is doubtful if the toad, *Bufo marinus*, is attacked by the mongoose. However, Williams (1918) found toad remains in 14 of the 180 stomachs of the small Indian mongoose that he examined in Trinidad. *Bufo marinus* was introduced into the Hawaiian Islands in April, 1932. Its remains are not found in mongoose stomachs in proportion to its abundance. The poison of this toad is a mixture of (1) marinobufagin that has a digitalis-like action and also causes ventricular fibrillation, (2) marinobufotoxin that is more emetic than the bufagin, and (3) marinobufotenine with an oxytocic action. Judd (in Baldwin *et al.*, 1952) confined 6 toads with 6 mongooses in a large box. A day later four toads had been eaten but one mongoose was dead, probably from injuries caused when it was trapped. Further toads, making an overall total of 21, were placed in the box with the 5 remaining mongooses. In 11 days the five mongooses ate 20 toads and showed no ill effects.

CENTIPEDES AND SCORPIONS

The small Indian mongoose will feed on scorpions and centipedes when these are available. In 98 stomachs from St Croix and Puerto Rico there were centipedes in 38 (Wolcott, 1953), and in 180 stomachs from Trinidad there were centipedes in 14 and a scorpion in one (Williams, 1918). Fischer (1921) says that *Herpestes edwardsi* seems to be immune to the poison of centipedes and scorpions, and it not only takes no precautions when catching them but often plays with the scorpions. Sometimes the scorpion is so carried that its sting is against the cheek of the mongoose. The mongoose eats the poison bulb and the sting, which it seems to consider a *bonne bouche.* In experiments with a scorpion, *Opisthophthalmus latimanus* Koch, a species that stridulates to warn its attackers, it was found that a meerkat always killed it so fast that it had no time to stridulate (Alexander, 1958).

Centipedes are probably quite unable to bite through the tough skin of a mongoose. One of us has tried to get individuals of the largest British centipede to bite, but the only place the jaws could penetrate was the soft skin of the lobe of the ear. A bite on the ear felt like a very mild nettle sting.

Some arthropods with powerful defensive glands are, however, not often taken by mongooses. For instance, Williams found only one millipede in the 180 stomachs he examined.

III

Reproduction and parental care

THE only detailed account of the reproductive cycle of a mongoose under natural conditions is that of Pearson & Baldwin (1953) for the small Indian mongoose in Hawaii. They found that the male may become sexually mature in as little as about four months. At this time the testes contain all stages of spermatogenesis and spermiogenesis, including spermatozoa. Once the testes of the male becomes mature in the late summer or autumn of the year of birth it continues to contain spermatozoa and all stages of spermatogenesis for the rest of the life of the individual. It may be noted that males that become sexually mature in the year that they were born will not find sexually mature females of their own age until the following spring. Despite the ability to produce spermatozoa in every month of the year, the testes undergo a slight but definite seasonal fluctuation in size, being largest in February and March and again at the beginning of the breeding season. The unusual mechanism of sex determination in *Herpestes* is described by Fredga (1965a, b).

Breeding females are found from the end of February until early September. Because fertile males are present at all times of the year, the limits of the breeding season are determined by the females. In Hawaii they have two litters a year: every female was pregnant or lactating in March and April and again in June and July. The first litter is usually born in April and the second in July. The female may become pregnant when it is as young as nine months. Females usually mate in the spring following the year of their birth, but those of the second litter probably mate a little later in the season. The second oestrus is post-lactational.

The uterus is bipartite, and the horns are 20 to 30 mm long. Cleaving ova may pass from one horn to the other. After parturition, implantation scars may remain visible for as long as four months. Ovulation apparently does not occur in the absence of copulation. The duration of pregnancy is about seven weeks, a figure also given by Powell (1913) for the same species in India. It is not known whether the duration of pregnancy is affected by day-length as it is, for instance, in the mink. A litter usually consists of two to four, but as many as five have been recorded (Bryan, 1908). A cycle of ossification and de-ossification of the pubic symphysis is known to occur in a number of mammals. De-ossification facilitates parturition. Pearson & Baldwin have shown that in *H. auropunctatus* the bony symphysis pubis is resorbed during pregnancy, but before the end of lactation bone is again deposited so that the symphysis is reunited.

In the banded mongoose spermatozoa are first formed at about four months of age, but it is not known when the female first becomes sexually mature. In the ichneumon incomplete sexual behaviour, which did not lead to copulation, first took place when the males and females were 15 months old. It is not until both sexes of this species are very nearly two years old that they are sexually mature and the female shows the typical signs of being on heat, e.g. the vulva becomes swollen and red (Dücker, 1960). In general, the Viverridae mature more slowly than the more highly evolved carnivora, and the fossa (*Cryptoprocta*) does not become sexually mature until it is about five years old.

The gestation period of *H. edwardsi* is about eight or nine weeks and that of the meerkat about eleven weeks. The female may come on heat very shortly after parturition, e.g. ten days later in the ichneumon and as little as five days later in the meerkat. In most species there is usually a litter of two or three, but four is quite common and five is recorded in *H. auropunctatus* and the meerkat and six in *Mungos mungo* and *Helogale parvula*. Most species have two litters a year, one in the spring and the other in the late summer, but in some latitudes some species may have litters in any month of the year, e.g. *H. edwardsi*. According to Dücker (1960), ichneumon gives birth standing up with the hind legs slightly bent.

Apart from the accounts by Dücker (1962) and Ewer (1963a, b) of the meerkat, little is known about the growth of young mongooses. The eyes begin to open on the tenth and are completely open by the twelfth day. In the Indian mongoose the eyes open after 16 to 17 days (Powell, 1913). After 14 days they are completely covered by hair, but it is not until two months that they are coloured like the parents. On the fifth day two incisors could be felt on the upper jaw, on the eleventh the upper and lower jaws had four incisors, and 30 days after birth the milk dentition of the meerkat is complete.

They began to take solid food when they were 22 days old. The weight of two female meerkats reared by Dücker increased as follows:

Days after birth	*Weight in grams*	
	A	B
0	40	43
3	55	57
8	78	77
11	90	85
14	100	98
17	120	115
20	125	125
24	142	145
29	163	165
37	180	190
50	215	210
62	245	242

PARENTAL CARE

The mother helps the young to suckle by pulling them near to her. After their eyes open, she may invite them to suckle by sitting up and turning her belly towards them. When the young are older, she may prevent them from suckling by threatening them or by lying on her belly so that they cannot get at her teats. Their last attempt to suckle was made 58 days after birth.

It has been found that during the first few days after birth each kitten of the domestic cat gradually establishes ownership of one teat and then rarely sucks from another. In the pig some degree of teat ownership is also established. The suckling behaviour of the meerkat has been described by Ewer (1963b). When the young are first born, the female crouches over them in such a way that it is impossible to determine their feeding positions. However, as they become larger the female can no longer suckle them in this position, and by the third week she begins to lie on her back to feed them (Fig. 3A). Three young were observed by Ewer between the 17th and 32nd day after birth. Movements of the fore paws against the mammary glands were sometimes made by the young as they fed. Occasionally a short series of alternate thrusts of the two paws occurred, but these never developed into the strong and definite 'milk tread' of young domestic cats.

The meerkat has three pairs of teats, the anterior pair being slightly larger than the others and the posterior pair slightly smaller. Each kitten sucked from each teat, and no 'ownership' was apparent, but there was a tendency for one teat to be favoured over the others. Thus, although there was no teat constancy, the young have the ability to recognise particular teats, and each tends to select a particular teat at the beginning of the feeding period. This, however, does not result in the development of ownership. As Ewer points out, the situation in the meerkat is of some interest in that specific teat recognition must develop before teat constancy can be achieved. The meerkat therefore probably represents a primitive condition

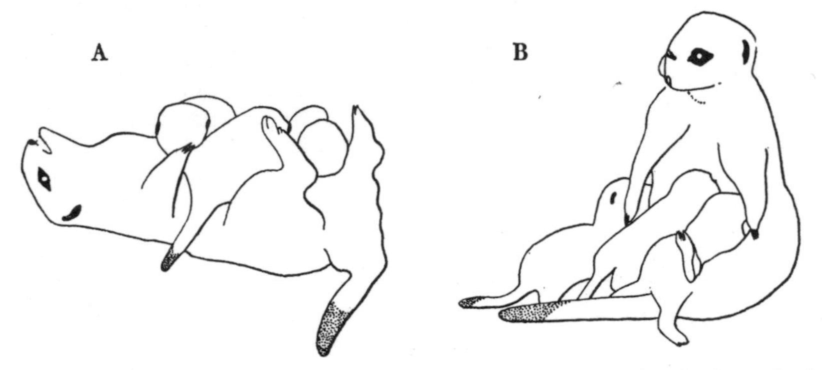

Fig. 3. Mother meerkat feeding her young. Lying on her back to feed them (A) and feeding them in the lazy-sit position (B). (After Ewer)

similar to that from which the more specialised organisation of such animals as the domestic cat must have been evolved.

When the young begin to eat other food they are often treated by the mother as competitors. When they are about a month old they begin to show jealousy over food, taking food from each other and making a threatening sound all the while. Dücker's young began to chase locusts when they were 50 days old, and they caught their first live mouse when they were 78 days old.

The mother meerkat may carry the young either by the head or neck (Fig. 4) as a cat carries her kittens or by the middle of the body like a rat carries her young. Sometimes one female will consistently use one method and another the other. When the young are larger, carrying them by the middle of the body becomes difficult, and the mother may then take hold of them by the skin of the thigh.

Dücker found that the two young she had purred both when

feeding and when cradled gently in her hand. Ewer was unable to detect any purring in the young. Powell (1913) says that the young of the Indian mongoose purr like a cat when they are suckling, and that the mother also purred but only when drinking milk.

Young meerkats, like those of most mammals that have nests, are at first unable to micturate or defaecate without external stimulation, which is provided by the female licking the perineal region. Care of the rest of the body is provided by the mother fleaing and licking. The mother may sometimes use her claws to part their hair so that she can reach the skin with her teeth (Dücker, 1962). There is some individual variation in this behaviour, and two female meerkats never cleaned their young by general licking over the whole body (Ewer, 1963a).

The male meerkat observed by Ewer did not undertake any toilet duties for his first litter but spent much time grooming his second litter, although he did not lick them. In addition to direct defence of the young against possible enemies, the male showed a general tendency to guard them. While they were still too young to leave the sleeping box, he was never absent for very long and would return to them at frequent intervals from whatever part of the house he happened to be. The young were given away when 12 weeks old, and, although the mother did not seem disturbed, the male '. . . ran uneasily hither and thither about the house, apparently searching for them'. When the young of his first litter started to play actively, the male joined in their games although the mother rarely did so. According to Ewer, this difference was partly due to the fact that the mother was three years old but the male was still quite young and playful. However, when the male was three years old and had virtually given up playing, he would join in the play

Fig. 4. Mother meerkat carrying 16 day old young. (After Ewer)

of his young litter although less frequently than he had with other litters when he was younger.

One of the most interesting patterns of parental behaviour observed by Ewer concerned the feeding behaviour of the female meerkat. When the litter was four weeks old she would snatch food from them even though she had just fed and could not have been very hungry. This behaviour changed radically, and at six weeks a new feeding pattern had developed. The mother would now run back and forth with a piece of food in her mouth as if enticing the young to take it. At this age they showed intense food envy and so would dash up to her and snatch the food from her mouth. When the mother was given food while the young were all busy eating, she would not eat it herself but would run from one to another of the litter and finally lay the morsel beside one of the young. The same pattern was observed when she was given insects. Ewer points out that this was an innate pattern performed without comprehension because even when the dish was full and all the young were eating, she would not herself eat but would carry the food to the young regardless of the fact that they were already well supplied. Observation of another litter showed that this pattern first began to appear when the young were 22 days old: the female took food to where the young were but ate it herself. By the 30th day she had started to give food to the young. By the 5th week, even when foraging in the garden, most of the prey caught was given to the young. By the 10th week the tendency of the mother to feed the young although still present is much less evident and is clearly waning.

The behaviour described in the preceding paragraph makes clear the biological significance of food envy. As Ewer says, 'The young respond to the sight of another individual with food by attempting to snatch it away. As a result, not only are they easily fed by the mother whose greater strength and experience make her much more adept at finding insects, but if she has discovered any slightly unusual type of food they too quickly learn to eat it. In such omnivorous creatures as meerkats this may be of considerable importance. In the domestic situation this is easily demonstrated. The young of both litters, when first offered banana, did not recognise it as food and showed no interest in it. However, when the mother was given banana in their presence they snatched it from her and ate and thereafter accepted it as food and soon became extremely fond of it. In this way *food traditions* in relation to whatever happens to be locally available could easily be established and handed on.'

The meerkat family is a social unit in which both parents are of importance. The young are fed only by the female, both before and after weaning. The male is important as a guard and defender of the group. His grooming of the young and his participation in their games also strengthen the social bonds of the group.

IV
Life span

NEARLY all men may expect to live between seventy and eighty years barring accidents and diseases of one kind or another. Each kind of animal also has a typical life span: even under the best conditions it will not live beyond a certain time. This is not to say that under the same conditions some individuals will not live longer than others of the same species. Birth certificates were introduced into Britain in 1837, and certified records exist of people living 109 years. Thus the men who have lived the longest have lived only about half again longer than most men can expect to live.

Probably very few if any wild animals live out their potential life span. Nearly all are killed by enemies or diseases before they have become particularly old. In his *History of Life and Death* Bacon said, 'In Beasts domestic, the degenerate life doth corrupt—in wild, their exposing to the fury of all weathers often intercepteth them.' However, domesticity does not corrupt the mongoose, and the dangers to it of a free life are much greater than might be supposed.

Some zoo records (e.g. Flower, 1931) of the length of life of different kinds of mongooses are as follows:

Species	*Years*
Herpestes edwardsi	8
Herpestes auropunctatus	7
Herpestes smithi	6
Herpestes vitticollis	13
Herpestes ichneumon	7·5
Herpestes pulverulentus	8·6
Mungos mungo	8·5
Ichneumia albicauda	10
Bdeogale crassicauda	10·9
Cynictis penicillata	12
Suricata suricatta	6

Zoo records of the length of life of animals are well known for their unreliability. We feel more confident about those relating to personal pets, where confusion between different individuals is so much less likely.

A ruddy mongoose (*H. smithi*), kept as a pet from the age of about three months, lived for 17 years and 11 months, having become rather fat and lost some of its teeth at the end (Phillips, 1956). A female of the same species captured as an adult was kept as a pet from April 1931 to 1946 and then sent to Regent's Park Zoo, where it died in June 1947. At the time of its death this mongoose was at least 16 years and 2 months old (Hill, 1956).

Nothing is known about the length of life of the ruddy mongoose in nature, but we do know something of this for the small Indian mongoose. Pearson & Baldwin (1953) trapped 144 male mongooses in Hawaii. One in ten males was estimated to be about three and a half years old. By this time they were practically toothless. The incisors were completely gone in most, and the canines were mere stumps. In many the molar surfaces were completely worn away, leaving only the roots which could scarcely have protruded above the gums. It is hardly likely that these toothless individuals could have survived, say, another year. Indeed, Pearson and Baldwin rightly comment on the surprising number of aged individuals in the wild population. Thus it would appear that in captivity exceptional individuals live four or more times as long as they do in the wild: so much for the alleged corruption of domesticity.

It is probable that wild mongooses in Hawaii live longer than in their native land because they do not have to contend with many of their natural enemies. All that we know about the length of life of wild animals suggests that this is so. For instance, Snyder (1956) has shown that in Michigan only one in a thousand white-footed mice (*Peromyscus*) could be expected to live 1·8 years, whereas in captivity they live six to eight years. Similarly, Harrison (1956) has shown that in the Malayan jungles no more than about 5 per cent of a number of different kinds of native rats live as much as one year.

A potential life span of about 17 years for the mongoose seems reasonable. The domestic cat has been known to live as long as 27 years, dogs rarely live as long as 20, rabbits in captivity live 10 to 15 years, and guinea pigs 6 to 8. Alex Comfort points out that the oldest thoroughbred mare in the British Stud Book, Bluebell, by Heron out of Jessie, died at the age of 34, although ponies have been known to live a little longer.

Within a species, or amongst very closely related species, the larger breeds are almost always shorter-lived than the smaller. But amongst those that are very unlike the small may live as long as the large; in Holland the bat, *Myotis mystacinus*, occasionally lives 20 years, which is as long as any dog.

Apart from man the only mammal definitely known to exceed 50 years is the elephant. We have accepted published records of 16 and 17 years for the length of life of the ruddy mongoose. However, it may be that we have paid too little attention to Bacon's comment, 'Touching the length or shortness of life in Beasts, the knowledge which may be had is slender, the Observation negligent, the Tradition fabulous.'

V
Attack and defence

EXCEPT when mongooses are killing their prey, attack behaviour unmixed with elements of defensive behaviour is not often seen. We have already described the way a mongoose behaves when it is attacking and killing snakes and rats. Pure attack consists of a quick rush and very strong, uninhibited biting. An enemy or source of danger generally produces a conflict of tendencies to attack and to escape that may result in a variety of rather characteristic behaviour patterns.

Ultimate defence posture

When an enemy presses home an attack to the limit, mongooses, like other Viverridae and carnivores in general, throw themselves on their back. In this position the vulnerable nape of the neck is protected and the claws and teeth are directed towards the aggressor (Plate IVc, facing p. 15). The bushy tail with the hairs erected may be placed over its belly and head so that the head, which may be largely concealed, looks out at the adversary from amongst the hairs of the tail.

The Indian mongoose, *H. edwardsi*, sometimes assumes a defensive posture which is quite unlike that of other mongooses even of the same genus, e.g. *H. javanicus* and *H. ichneumon*. When attacked, the Indian mongoose will often form a complete ball. It places its head between its legs and its bushy tail with the hairs erected over its back. In this position its head, which is largely concealed, looks out at the adversary from amongst the hairs of the hind legs and the base of the tail (Plate IVB, facing p. 15). The enemy is thus presented with the parts of its body that have the longest hair, the tail and the sacral and lumbar regions of the back. Rensch & Dücker have drawn attention to the fact that the lumbar vertebrae, which form the part of the back turned to the enemy, are greatly modified as compared with the two other species of *Herpestes* they examined (Plate V, opposite). The transverse processes or projections of the lumbar region are greatly broadened and lengthened. For instance, the width of the seventh lumbar vertebra is equal to 55 per cent of the maximum width of the pelvis in the male and 48 per cent in the female. In *H. javanicus* and *H. ichneumon* the comparable percentages are 34 and 44 respectively. The maximum width of the transverse process of the seventh lumbar vertebra is 16 per cent of the maximum width of the pelvis in the male and 14 per cent in the female. In *H. javanicus* and *H. ichneumon* the comparable figures are 11 and 8 per cent respectively.

The remarkably enlarged processes of the lumbar vertebrae of the Indian mongoose were probably evolved *pari passu* with the habit of rolling up; as a result it is the protected lumbar region that is exposed to the enemy. Rensch & Dücker believe that rolling up into a ball, which also frequently occurs in fight and defence playing, may be taken up when fighting with a cobra that is attacking from above. We hardly think that this is likely: there is certainly nothing to suggest it in the accounts of fights between the cobra and the Indian mongoose.

ENCOUNTERS WITH OTHER SPECIES

Ewer (1963a) has given a good account of the behaviour of the meerkat in the presence of predators of various kinds, and unless otherwise indicated, the remarks that follow apply to the meerkat.

Predators on the ground. The sight of an enemy on the ground, such as a strange dog, usually evokes an erection of the hair. This is normally accompanied by stretching the legs and arching the back, with the tail held stiffly erect and the head slightly lowered: the change is dramatic. What was a long and low-slung animal is suddenly converted into one that is apparently much larger and much fatter. In its new shape the meerkat may now move towards the enemy in what Ewer has called a 'stiff-legged rock'. It advances at a gallop but keeps its back arched and its legs stiff, a gait which is a compromise between a tendency to attack and a tendency to avoid doing so. Although it appears to advance at a gallop, it covers little ground because it jumps high in the air at each step. In so doing it presents a very alarming appearance in that it see-saws up and down at each step (Fig. 5). It usually keeps growling as it moves towards the enemy.

If in spite of this behaviour the enemy approaches more closely,

Plate V. The lumbar, sacral, and caudal vertebrae of species of *Herpestes*. (A) *H. javanicus* (*H. auropunctatus* ?). (B) *H. ichneumon*. (C) *H. edwardsi* showing the unusually wide transverse processes of the lumbar vertebrae. (After Rensch and Dücker)

Plate VI. An example of a staged fight between a mongoose and a snake. These are common tourist attractions in parts of India. The snake, always said to be very poisonous, is commonly a harmless species.

the meerkat growls furiously and comes to a stand. It may then move slowly backwards and then again advance and thrust its head towards the enemy with a sudden explosive spit. This type of behaviour does not usually result in a real bite being delivered, but sometimes a dog may be caused to run away by being bitten on the nose.

When the enemy is not dangerously near, displacement digging may occur. Displacement digging differs from normal digging in

Fig. 5. Stiff-legged rock of the meerkat drawn from successive frames. In the series taken from the side (1 to 9) the intensity is greater and the hind legs are more raised than in the series (A to H) taken from behind. (After Ewer)

that it is done with both front feet together while the meerkat is looking at the enemy instead of the ground. Displacement digging may occur whenever the meerkat is agitated: the sight of an enemy or a strange person is often sufficient to induce it. As might be supposed, displacement digging only occurs where the substrate is suitable. It does not, for instance, occur on a tarred road. Ewer was able to demonstrate this easily by using an animal on a lead. Each time it was manoeuvred on to the grassy verge displacement digging commenced but stopped each time it was back on the tarred road.

By definition displacement behaviour is the performance of a behaviour pattern out of the particular functional context in which it normally occurs. It is generally exhibited when releasing stimuli for two or more different kinds of behaviour occur together, e.g. attack and escape, under conditions in which the consummatory act of neither can take place. This displacement or 'sparking-over' concept of Kortland is generally accepted. To describe a particular pattern of behaviour as displacement behaviour carries with it certain disadvantages: it defines and pigeon-holes a pattern of behaviour in such a way that the observer may tend not to look further into the matter and therefore not try to discover whether the so-called displacement behaviour has some quite different selective value.

As Ewer points out, it is to be expected that digging should be resorted to as displacement activity. In the first place, the threshold for digging is very low: the meerkat is almost always ready to dig, and the centre concerned with this activity requires very little excitation. In the second place, the pattern of the stiff-legged rock not only includes simultaneous movement of the forelegs with little forward progression but also closely resembles the digging pattern. It may be noted that sometimes displacement activity of one kind tends to be triggered simply because the animal assumes for some reason the appropriate posture. For instance, Dücker (1957) found that genets would often stretch when some other activity brought them into the appropriate posture for stretching.

Sometimes a displacement activity may be so ritualised that it comes to have a selective value it did not originally possess. It may, for instance, serve as a warning to members of the same species. However, in the meerkat the stiff-legged rock has apparently in no way been ritualised to serve as a warning to other meerkats even though it is regularly exhibited in any danger situation. Ewer probably quite rightly suggests that this has not occurred because the vocal warning cries of the meerkat already deal quite adequately with the situation.

Ewer found that her meerkats often deliberately left the shelter of the garden, in which foraging facilities were adequate, to go on to the road where dogs were certain to be found. She got the impression that there was a pleasurable component in these hostile encounters between her meerkats and dogs. We may note that it has been suggested that there is a kind of behavioural symbiosis between domestic dogs and cats (Spurway, 1953). The cat provides the dog with something on which to expend its pent-up hunting drive and the cat thereby secures a releaser for its escape patterns. Introspectively we know that we sometimes seek out situations involving a certain amount of danger, and there is reason to believe that some animals do the same.

Aerial predators. Meerkats live in open country in small communities, often with the ground squirrel (*Geosciurus*) whose burrows they may take over although they are capable of digging their own. Because of the open nature of the country in which they live, and because they are strictly diurnal, hawks and eagles are said to be their commonest enemies.

They must constantly guard against attack from the air (Heck, 1956). A hawk, even high in the air, does not pass unnoticed, and

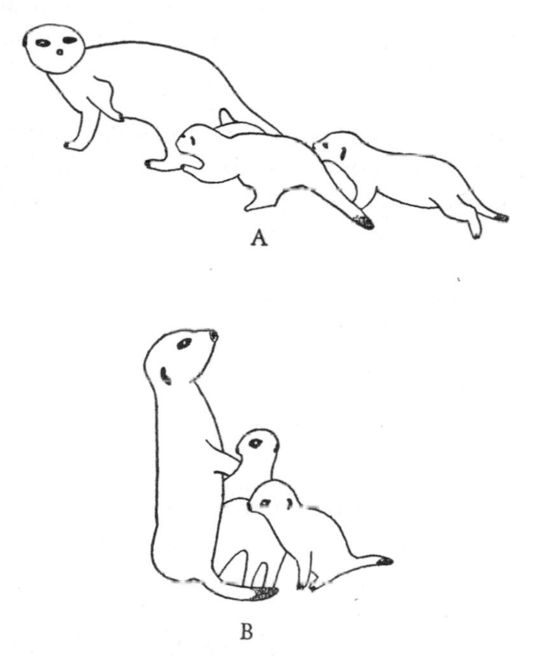

Fig. 6. Response of young meerkats seven weeks old to alarm call of the mother evoked by the presence of a hawk. (A) The mother moves cautiously to greater safety and the young follow closely. (B) The young stay close to the mother while she watches the hawk. (After Ewer)

the alarm call is given and the hawk is watched until it flies away or it becomes evident that it is not going to attack. When birds harmless to them appear in the sky they are given a quick glance and then ignored, although very occasionally a harmless bird will evoke an alarm call.

The responses of the meerkat to aerial predators are very complex and include not only an innate component but also changes that accompany maturation as well as learning by experience.

Innate behaviour towards aerial predators probably includes a tendency to look upwards and to respond by flight or alarm calling. At first this is probably quite unspecific and only later do they learn by experience which birds are dangerous. Meerkats reared in Africa as pets often see hawks but were never attacked by them. They nevertheless give the alarm call and remain vigilant in the presence of a hawk even when harmless birds have ceased to evoke a response (Fig. 6). As Ewer remarks, this suggests that either (1) there is some innate mechanism that prevents the waning of the response to the particular shape of a hawk even in the absence of any experience of attack, or (2) that meerkats only accept birds as harmless that both fly low and fail to attack.

When a year-old and a three-year-old meerkat saw an aeroplane for the first time they were thrown into a panic and fled to shelter. After a few times, however, flight gave way to vigilant watching, the alarm cry being given as long as the aeroplane was in sight. The male meerkat soon learned to recognise the approach of the aeroplane by its sound. It would then run to a look-out position from which the aeroplane was watched until it vanished from sight, the alarm call being given all the time. Sight seemed to be more important than sound in the response to aeroplanes. The intensity of the alarm call would fall off as soon as an approaching plane altered course.

ENCOUNTERS BETWEEN INDIVIDUALS OF THE SAME SPECIES

A strange mongoose introduced into a cage with others of its species may be more or less seriously attacked by them. Under such conditions a strange meerkat may be killed. Even when two individuals of opposite sex are brought together for the first time there may be some fighting. Pimental (1955a) found that if two freshly caught *H. auropunctatus* were placed in a cage there was no fighting, but when an individual was introduced to one already established in the cage, whether of opposite sex, or whether both were females, serious fighting developed and one or both were killed. In meerkats two very distinctive patterns of behaviour seem to have been evolved that serve to prevent serious damage from intraspecific fighting: back-attack and inhibited biting (Ewer, 1963).

Back-attack. In both defence and attack the meerkat may turn around and move rump first towards another. This behaviour normally occurs only in encounters with other meerkats. It is exhibited by both young and adults. An interesting exception was noted by Ewer: back-attack was used against cats by pet meerkats that had accepted the cats in the same household more or less as fellows or at least not as dangerous enemies. Back-attack is sometimes used in play fighting with another meerkat or a domestic cat (Fig. 7).

Back-attack behaviour seems to be an elaboration of the normal back turning employed by a meerkat to prevent another from stealing its food, when it turns around rapidly to present its rump to the would-be thief and so keeps the food out of reach. One animal may keep others from the dish of food for a time by rapidly turning around and around and fending them off with its rump.

In *H. edwardsi* a similar back turning has been described, but in this species it is less evolved and used only for defence (Dücker, 1957). It seems likely that the defensive attack pattern of the crab-eating mongoose, which can squirt a copious and foul smelling fluid from the anal glands for a considerable distance, has been evolved from a back-attack pattern accompanied by a tendency to mark when excited, which is so common amongst different kinds of mongooses. The defensive attack of the skunk has probably been evolved in a similar manner. Although little is known about the defensive attack behaviour of the crab-eating mongoose, it would seem to be intermediate between that of the skunk and, say, the meerkat. The back defence and/or attack pattern has been observed in a few other carnivores such as martens and dogs.

Fig. 7. Back attack position of a meerkat in a play fight with a half grown cat. (After Ewer)

Inhibited biting. Inhibited biting is of great importance because it prevents mutual damage. When exhibiting this type of behaviour, the meerkat holds its jaws firmly closed, and the head is thrust towards the partner and moved rapidly from side to side. As the side to side movements of the head are made, an attempt is made to bring the head into contact with the partner so that the chin or side of the face is rubbed against the other individual. Ewer likens the effect to two fencers sparring for an opening. In *H. edwardsi* the top of the head is rubbed against the partner rather than the chin or cheek. Rensch & Dücker interpret this as an invitation to play, as does Dücker (1962) in the meerkat. However, as Ewer points out, this pattern of behaviour occurs in many situations that have nothing to do with play. What is common to all situations in which this type of behaviour occurs is that a strong tendency to bite is combined with a social inhibition against biting.

Meerkats often show inhibited biting when a member of the family returns after a prolonged absence or when being gradually accustomed to the presence of a stranger. A female introduced to a male was very aggressive and attempted to drive him away by genuine attempts to bite interspersed with inhibited biting. Although in this instance the male could easily have killed the female, it responded only by back-attack and inhibited biting.

Ewer believes that inhibited biting originated by elaboration from the normal movements of the head that are made when sniffing and digging for food. The suggestion was made because on several occasions it was observed that when a meerkat foraging for food looked up and saw a dog, and if at the same time its chin came into contact with the vegetation, it would sometimes go over into the inhibited biting pattern. In fact, under these circumstances all intermediate patterns have been exhibited between normal food-finding head movements and inhibited biting. The sight of an enemy is an uncomplicated situation and never evokes inhibited biting. It therefore appears that the addition of the food-finding component to the aggression evoked by the sight of an enemy results in inhibited biting. This hypothesis seems the more likely when we consider the fact that during food-finding the strong stimulus to bite provided by the smell of the food is firmly inhibited, as witness the fact that food is not bitten until it is completely dug out and if necessary made harmless by a preliminary clawing.

VI
Sexual and some other types of behaviour

SEXUAL BEHAVIOUR

THE sexual behaviour of only two species, the ichneumon (Dücker, 1960) and the meerkat (Ewer, 1963a), has been described in any detail. In the ichneumon the behaviour that precedes mating always begins with the male pursuing the female. During pursuit the male makes *e-e-e* sounds which the female repeats. Outside the mating season such sounds are a general expression of a desire for social contact. The female often crouches for a short time but then runs away as the male approaches. This crouching and running

Fig. 8. Mating position of the meerkat. (After Ewer)

away always precedes the assumption of the mating position. At times it seems clearly to be used for enticing the male. When crouching is omitted, the female is often pressed down by the male with his mouth.

When the female is not ready to mate, she often remains in a crouching position so that it is not possible for the male to mount her. When the female is ready to mate, she assumes the mating position immediately after crouching. This position is achieved by straightening the hind legs, raising the hind quarters, turning the tail sideways at a right angle, and lowering the head. When mounting, the male embraces the middle of the female's body with his fore legs (Fig. 8).

Before successful mating, attempts at mounting may be repeated several times at ever shortening intervals. During the latter stages excitement greatly increases and is distinguished by the appearance for the first time of the typical mating sound, *he-he-he*, which is made by both sexes. The frequency of the mating calls made by the male increases and is often replaced by a loud heckling sound. In the preliminary attempts at mating, which probably do not often result in ejaculation, the female is mounted for only a minute and a half to two minutes. When the male is successful, it usually remains mounted for four to five minutes. During this time it repeatedly pushes its widely open mouth on to the neck of the female, but there is no actual neck-biting.

The meerkat also does not use actual neck-biting during actual mating but may use it before mating. For instance, if the female repulses the male, he may grasp her firmly by the neck without, however, closing his jaws sufficiently to wound her. The male meerkat seems to use the neck grip simply in order to induce passivity in an aggressive female. Passivity in response to the neck grip is not confined to the female: individuals of either sex hang limply if one lifts them by the skin on the nape of the neck. In some Viverridae and Mustelidae the male grips the female by the neck with his mouth before mounting in order to block escape reactions. In the domestic cat the neck bite tends to become a ritual, and the male cannot successfully mount the female unless she gives in voluntarily. Leyhausen (1956) points out that in the cat family (Felidae) biting the nape of the neck occurs in four major behaviour patterns: (1) by either sex when killing prey; (2) by a male when attacking a rival; (3) by a male when mating; and (4) by a female when picking up and carrying the young.

Attempts by the meerkat to mate may be preceded by bouts of semi-serious fighting. As in many other animals, dogs for instance, there is a tendency for the general excitation of rough play to go over into sexual behaviour. In these bouts one meerkat may bite at the nose of the other and grip it between its jaws. The partner's nose is not gripped hard enough to cause damage. The significance of nose biting in meerkats is not understood. Unlike the ichneumon, the female meerkat does not appear to adopt any specific posture in order to facilitate mating.

When a young female meerkat on heat is with an old male, she may attempt to incite him. Ewer found that a young female would sometimes attempt to incite a male that was three years old and no longer very active sexually. She did this by nipping at him, particularly at the tufts of hairs on his cheeks. This usually led to a bout of semi-serious fighting. When the general level of excitation of the male had been sufficiently raised, he would attempt to mount.

TOILET BEHAVIOUR

No species of mongoose appears to have an elaborate toilet ritual. The rather coarse fur is kept clean by being rubbed during passage through narrow openings or, in burrowing forms such as the meerkat, by moving through the burrows. When necessary, other activities are briefly interrupted in order to clean parts of the body. Face washing, such as occurs in the Viverrinae, has not been observed in any mongoose, but pieces of dirt adhering to the face are brushed off with one paw or sometimes both paws used simultaneously, more rarely alternately. The movement of the paw or paws is forwards and downwards from eyes to snout. If bits of food have become lodged between the teeth, they are removed by *Herpestes edwardsi*, *Mungos mungo*, *Suricata*, and probably all species, with the claws of the fore feet. Speaking of an Indian mongoose, Sterndale (1884, p. 224) says, 'He was excessively clean, and after eating would pick his teeth with his claws in a most absurd manner.'

The head, ears, chin, neck, flanks, and back are cleaned mainly by scratching with the hind legs, the parts that are to be cleaned being bent towards the hind foot (Dücker, 1965). The flanks and, so far as is possible, also the back are nibbled with the incisors or the fur combed with them. An irritation of the skin is dealt with by scratching with the hind foot or by nibbling at it with the incisors. The chest, belly, front and hind legs, between the toes, the tail, and the anal and genital parts are cleaned exclusively with the mouth. The positions assumed during cleaning are very variable. The belly and anal and genital regions are usually cleaned while sitting or lying on the back. Usually when cleaning in a sitting position, the weight is placed on one side, and the hind leg of the opposite side is stretched almost vertically upwards at the same time as the body is bent forwards. When cleaning while sitting normally, the head may be pushed between the front legs or along one front leg to the rear. Sometimes while sitting one fore leg is lifted while the other touches the ground with the toes only. When cleaning while lying on the back, the hind part of the body bends upwards and forwards and there is a simultaneous lifting of the head to reach the rear.

Mutual grooming. Nibbling with the incisors can very easily be evoked in the meerkat by tickling any part of the body. The area just above the root of the tail is particularly sensitive to tickling (Ewer, 1963a). When tickled, the meerkat does not nibble at the area stimulated but at whatever area the mouth happens to be nearest. It is thus very easy to induce it to nibble one's hand. This response, which is released by chance tactile stimuli, of course leads to mutual grooming between individuals. Kinloch (1964) once observed a pet banded mongoose grooming a patas monkey through the bars of the latter's cage. Mutual nibbling usually begins on that part of the body which happens to offer itself. When one individual begins to nibble, the other at once reciprocates, and mutual grooming may continue for sometime and evidently has a social bond-maintaining function.

Defaecation and urination. The mongooses, unlike many Viverrinae, do not dig holes and bury their droppings. A few ill-defined scratching movements may be made, but there is a lot of variation amongst species and individuals in the amount of scratching. The species of *Herpestes* often change the site of defaecation but also frequently revisit places that have been used. The striped-necked mongoose seems to have a favourite rock on which it defaecates, the rock in time becoming covered with droppings (Hutton, 1948). Species that live in colonies, such as *Cynictis* (Roberts, 1951), have sites that are used by the whole colony as lavatories. When meerkats are about 10 weeks old defaecation begins to take on a social character: once a site is selected, all of the litter use it so that in time a communal pile of droppings is produced (Ewer, 1963a). When defaecating, meerkats and other mongooses spread their hind legs and press down the hind part of the body while raising the tail. Females assume the same posture when urinating, but the male lifts one hind leg and usually urinates against a vertical plane in the manner of a dog.

MARKING

In common with most other Viverridae, mongooses have anal scent glands. In mongooses there are two (Fig. 9), which usually open in a pouch or sac-like depression outside the anus proper. The secretion of the glands is stored in the pouch. In *Herpestes* and allied genera a pair of anal scent glands is present in both sexes.

Similar glands are present in the male meerkat but are absent in the female. The morphology and histology of the anal glands of *H. ichneumon*, *Ichneumia*, and *Mungos mungo* have been described (Chatin, 1874; Ortmann, 1960; Schaffer, 1940). Ortmann has summarised what is known about their structure. His photographs of sections through the glands of *Ichneumia* are not very useful because it is impossible to distinguish cell boundaries.

In some species such as the striped-necked mongoose, the scent is particularly offensive to humans. It may be noted here that the scent or musk called civet that is used in the perfume industry and sometimes in medicine is obtained from the anal glands of several genera of Viverrinae (*Civettictis*, *Viverra*, *Viverricula*). These are tamed and kept in captivity in order to obtain the scent. The African civet, *C. civetta*, produces a total of three to four grams a

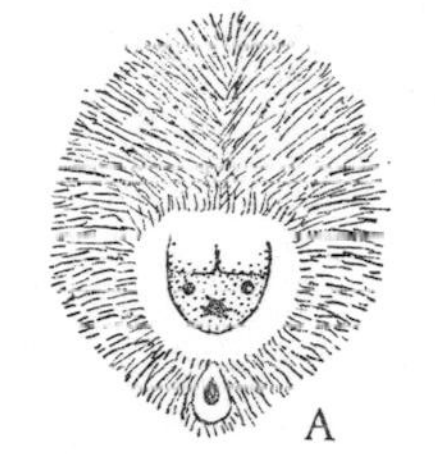

Fig. 9. Female of *Helogale parvula* showing (A) the anal sac partly distended and the openings of the two anal glands, one on either side of the anus. (B) Closed anal sac of the same species. (After Pocock)

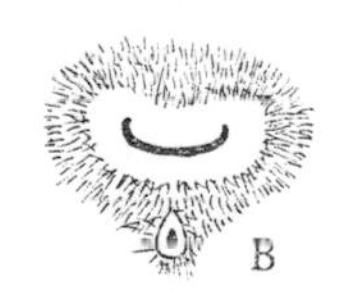

week, the musk being removed several times each week. In India the musk of *Viverricula indica*, which is removed by scraping the inside of the anal pouch, is used to flavour the tobacco that is smoked locally.

Although it is sometimes said that mongooses exhibit no territorial behaviour (e.g. Baldwin *et al.*, 1952), it would seem that the scent of the anal glands serves as a territorial pheromone. But in addition it may have other functions. For instance, in some of the brightly marked species such as the striped-necked mongoose, the scent functions in defence.

The marking behaviour of mongooses has been noted by a number of writers.* When marking most species lift one hind leg, evert

* Dücker (1957, 1962, 1965), Ewer (1963a), Fiedler (1957), Hediger (1949, 1950), Naundorff (1936), Pocock (1941), Prater (1935), and Rensch & Dücker (1959).

the rectal wall to expose the scent glands, and then rub the anal region on the site that is to be marked. Pets will mark projecting objects such as the corners of walls, edges of doors, and the entrance to the sleeping box. In nature the entrances to the burrows are repeatedly marked as are stones and other objects in their path while out hunting. Ewer found that her male meerkat when out for a walk would mark the corners of walls in the neighbourhood, and that these became regular marking points. If later the male passed close enough to one of these, it would sniff it and then renew

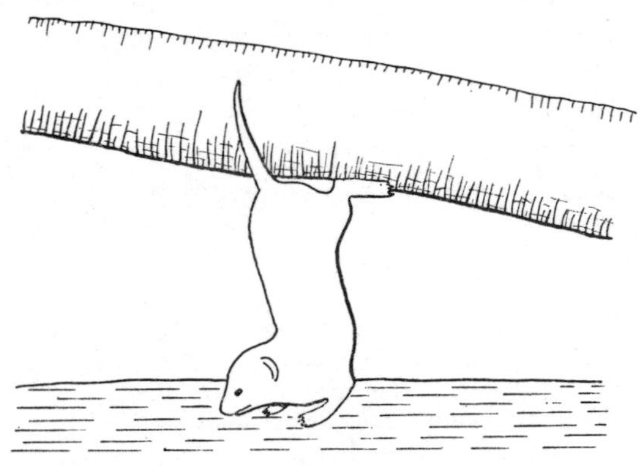

Fig. 10. Handstand marking position of the water mongoose, *Atilax paludinosus*. (After Hediger)

the mark. The male was able to detect its mark in the open after a lapse of a fortnight. Ewer found that female meerkats would sometimes exhibit marking behaviour, although they did not leave a mark because they lack scent glands. Whenever the male meerkat was excited or agitated, it would extensively mark the nearest vertical object. In these circumstances Ewer supposes that marking may have a displacement character, although it may serve as a warning signal to other meerkats visiting the site later.

In *Atilax*, as shown by Fiedler, marking is accomplished by standing on the front legs and rubbing the anal region on objects above the body (Fig. 10). A similar handstand position for marking is occasionally used by the female Indian mongoose, and it almost certainly is sometimes used by the male. Marking in the banded mongoose is accomplished by rubbing the anal region over the ground in a manner very similar to that of a badger or polecat.

In both sexes of *Herpestes edwardsi* a secretion is produced at the bases of the long hairs on each cheek about 15 mm from the mouth.

No such secretion occurs in *H. ichneumon* (Rensch & Dücker, 1959), nor does such a secretion appear to be recorded in any other mongoose. The secretion is produced by enlarged sebaceous glands. It smells like honey. In the polecat the whole fur smells similarly, and it is probable that over much of the body of the polecat the sebaceous glands produce a similar substance. In a pet polecat kept by one of us a strong musk smell masked any other kind of smell. In tame mongooses it was noted that projecting objects in a room were marked with the secretion by rubbing the cheeks against them, often during play fighting. Neither the significance of the secretion nor of the behaviour associated with it is known.

SITTING AND STRETCHING

Sitting postures have been most thoroughly described for the meerkat (Dücker, 1962, 1965; Ewer, 1963a; Haagner, 1920; Heck, 1956; Shortridge, 1935). In this species there are three sitting postures for which the names given by Ewer may be used:

(1) *Low-sit*. In this posture (Fig. 11A and Plate VIIA, facing p. 46) the meerkat is supported on the whole of the plantar surface of the pes. The tail is stretched out behind, and the back is vertical with a slight concavity immediately above the pelvis. The low-sit posture is very stable and may be held for a considerable time. It is used in sun-basking, particularly in the early morning when the sun is low. Among pets it is frequently adopted before an electric fire (Fig. 12). Low-sit is also used as a look-out posture.

(2) *High-sit*. In this posture the meerkat stands on its hind feet so that only the digits are in contact with the ground. The tip of the tail, which is held rigidly against the ground, provides extra support and acts like a third limb of a tripod (Fig. 11). The whole body is extended vertically as fully as possible. This posture was called the 'look-out' position by Shortridge. It gives maximum visual range. It is not much used in basking in the sun. Positions intermediate between low-sit and high-sit with maximum vertical extension also occur but only for relatively very short periods.

(3) *Lazy-sit*. In this posture (Fig. 3B) the meerkat sits on its hind quarters with the tail turned forwards between the legs and the body held loosely in a somewhat slouching manner. This posture is employed less often than low-sit or high-sit. It is generally used when the meerkat is resting but is sufficiently alert not to go to sleep, that is, when the animal is at ease and no great attention is being paid to its surroundings.

Shortridge notes that *Cynictis* uses the same low-sit and high-sit postures outside its burrows, but does not maintain them for as long as the meerkat. According to him, the banded mongoose uses the low-sit posture as a look-out one when hunting. The high-sit posture has been observed only in pets. Apparently neither *H. edwardsi* nor *M. mungo* use the lazy-sit posture, and the high-sit posture has not been observed in the former species.

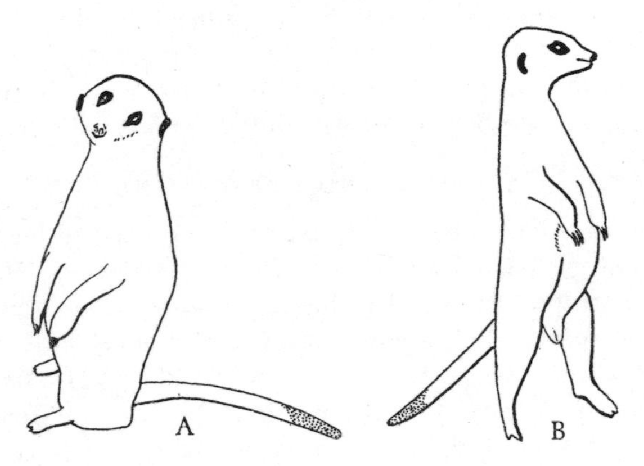

Fig. 11. Adult male meerkat in low-sit posture (A) and high-sit posture (B). (After Ewer)

Fig. 12. Adult male meerkat and three young seven weeks old basking in front of a fire. The young are showing the high-sit (A), low-sit (B), and the hearth rugging (C) postures. (After Ewer)

Plate VII(A). Low-sit posture of adult male meerkat.

Plate VII(B). Meerkat lying in front of an electric fire.

Plate VIII. Meerkats warming themselves in the morning sun. (After Heck)

After sleeping or after a prolonged rest *H. edwardsi* and *H. ichneumon* stretch both front legs far forwards and both back legs far backwards so that the belly lies close to the ground (Dücker, 1965). The meerkat sometimes also stretches in this manner, which is similar to that of the fox, polecat, and marten. Stretching is nearly always accompanied by yawning. A banded mongoose first stretched its front legs one by one and then its back legs one by one (Kinloch, 1964). The meerkat usually extends the front legs far forwards and the back is thrown in a downward arch just behind the shoulders. The rump is then somewhat elevated as the hind legs are extended. This usually completes the process of stretching, but sometimes the body is then brought forwards so that the front legs are almost vertical and the hind legs are stretched out behind (Ewer, 1963a). This kind of stretching is rather similar to the usual stretching of genets.

BEHAVIOURAL HEAT REGULATION

Behaviour that promotes either warming or cooling according to outward circumstance has been extensively described only for the meerkat (Ewer, 1963a). Heat exchanges occur more readily in the area of the belly because the hair here is much sparser than on the back. All of the heat regulatory postures therefore concern the relation of the belly to the environment.

Warming is done by exposing as much as possible of the ventral surface to the heat source. In the early morning sun or before a fire, the low-sit posture (see p. 45) is usually used (Plate VIIA, facing p. 46). When the sun is high or a fire is directed downward, the meerkat may lie flat on its back, or slightly to one side, with its legs spread. When the ground is warm, e.g. the floor in front of a fire, the meerkat lies on its belly with the body flattened, the hind legs spread sideways, and the front legs stretched out forwards on either side of the head (Fig. 12c).

In hot sunlight meerkats usually cease to be active before they have to pant. When it becomes too hot they seek out the shade and a cool surface on which to lie on their stomachs. If a cool surface is not available, they will sometimes scratch away the warm surface soil before lying down. Baldwin *et al.* (1952) have found that the rectal temperature of *H. auropunctatus* varies from 98·4°F when they are at rest in the shade to 105·3°F when they are extremely excited although still in the shade.

VII
Play

THE study of play behaviour in mammals is difficult: the significance of play has been interpreted in many different and often mutually exclusive ways, and it is difficult to distinguish some kinds of play behaviour from other sorts of behaviour. For these reasons, the background of the problem is considered briefly before the chief types of play behaviour of mongooses are described.

When we consider the anatomy of an animal we know that all structures have a function or have had a function in the past. When the relations between the animal and its environment change so that some structure ceases to have a function it is reduced, becomes vestigial, and in due course disappears: for it to be preserved or further evolved requires that it have a selective advantage that must more than compensate for the energy utilised in its production. Once we know the function of a structure we usually know or can guess its selective value. The same considerations would appear to apply to behaviour.

The functional approach to a study of structure has proved to be the most fruitful and effective approach, and there is reason to believe that it is the most effective approach to the study of play behaviour. We shall provisionally assume that all play behaviour patterns have a function and therefore a selective value. However, even when this assumption is made serious difficulties arise at other levels.

The behaviour that we classify as play in humans is mimicked by most of the higher mammals, especially carnivores and primates. Many of the behaviour patterns of these so closely resemble those of man in certain respects that two kinds of intellectual traps are, so to speak, set for us. Firstly, play behaviour in animals is described in the same terms as are used for play behaviour in man. This direct transference of terminology from one group to the other carries with it the danger that anthropomorphic interpretations are transferred together with the terminology. Secondly, the function or selective value of play in animals tends not unnaturally to be overlooked. One of the basic reasons for this is that in man the conception of play is generally opposed to the conception of work. The usefulness of this analogy can therefore depend upon the extent to which an animal can be said to 'work' in the sense that man 'works'.

It is possible to go too far in avoiding terminology that one thinks of as intrinsically anthropomorphic. Indeed it has to be demonstrated that it is not sometimes both correct and effective to describe some of the activities of the higher mammals in terms normally applicable to man, the most highly evolved mammal.

Play may be defined as a behaviour pattern that does not culminate in the type of consummatory act that is normally an end result of similar behaviour patterns should the opportunity arise. Play behaviour therefore normally appears to lack a goal. For instance, play fighting resembles true fighting but the animal indulges only in inhibited biting and not strong and damaging biting; flight play is distinguished from true flight in that the animal runs noisily away to its hiding place along an uncovered path, usually (*Herpestes*) with its tail raised, instead of moving silently along the shortest covered route to its hiding place.

It is a matter of common observation that play does not occur when the animal is under severe stress, whether this be physiological, e.g. hunger, or from its external environment, e.g. attack by a dangerous foe. But the animal is never, so to speak, in a vacuum, and even under the most favourable conditions it has to cope with some degree of environmental stress. It therefore follows that the stimuli necessary for the initiation of play must, if play is to occur, override conflicting stimuli. No qualitative, let alone quantitative, account of the level of stress that may be present during play has ever been given, and clearly this will vary enormously even in a single individual according to its stage of maturation, its previous history, and so forth. However, as is well known, play occurs more frequently in young animals still under parental care than in older animals. It is generally supposed that the reason for this is that the primary needs of the young animals are being cared for by the parents and so environmental stresses are at a relatively low level.

In young animals behaviour patterns generally classified as play resemble those of the mature animal, but they are less efficient and do not culminate in the consummatory act characteristic of adult behaviour. However, two serious difficulties may arise in this method of classifying behaviour: (1) the young animal may in fact be performing as efficiently as is possible for it at its particular level of development, and (2) a consummatory act may not occur simply because it cannot occur in the particular environment of the young animal as, for instance, in prey-catching play. When the function or selective advantage of a particular behaviour pattern is not understood, the temptation to classify it either as play or as a displacement activity is not always resisted.

Explanations of play that attribute its causation to an overflow of surplus energy tend to direct attention away from its possible selective value and leave us with the sterile hypothesis that it is its own motivation, that it is enjoyed for its own sake. Clearly scientific hypotheses that lead to further discoveries are better than those that do not if our object is to understand the natural world, and we may therefore dismiss hypotheses based purely on 'surplus energy' or 'self-reward'.

A widely held view of the selective value of play is that it enables the animal to practice and develop some degree of competence in dealing with certain contingencies before these become critical to its existence. Sometimes the objection is made that there is no evidence that animals prevented from playing are less efficient as adults than those that have not been prevented from playing. Because this kind of objection is often voiced in one form or another, it should be noted that there is no good experimental evidence that at the beginning of independent life there is parity between those animals that played and those that did not when they were dependent upon their parents. Furthermore such evidence would be excessively difficult to obtain for the following reason. The selective advantage that tends in the long run to preserve and develop a feature of an organism is said to be only 0·01, which means success in only one of ten thousand trials. Haldane (1932), for instance, has shown that a simple dominant with a selective advantage of only 0·1 per cent will establish itself in 50 per cent of the individuals of a population in 5000 generations. While it is not necessary to agree with the assumptions upon which such calculations have been made, nevertheless the general and we think correct view is that a structure or a habit conferring a very small degree of advantage in the struggle for existence will tend to be perserved. Certainly no one has attempted experiments at this level of accuracy between the abilities of animals that were allowed to play when young and those that were not. Furthermore, the selective advantage of play may possibly be restricted only to a short period of independent life when the animal for the first time has to cope with outward circumstance.

Mongooses like other mammals play most when young. As they become older, their readiness to play diminishes. Some species such as the meerkat seldom play by the time they are two years old. Nearly all that is known about play in mongooses may be found in the papers by Dücker (1965), Ewer (1963a), and Rensch & Dücker (1959).

Fighting play. This is the commonest form of play in all mongooses that have been studied. During it the animal is continually switching from attack to defence. The most frequently observed invitation to this kind of play is for the attacker to jump up and bite the fur of the partner. The importance of the invitation to play often seems to lie in the surprise visual effect of a particular movement. For instance, the ichneumon and the meerkat often get up on their hind legs and suddenly bear down on their partner from above. Short and jerky jumps on the spot or towards the partner may also initiate the game. Such jumps are often associated with sudden turnings of the body or, in *Herpestes*, with oscillating movements of the head. Many fighting games also begin with the animal 'taking stock' before the partner and then suddenly jumping forwards and recoiling again. The partner replies by a similar pretence attack and recoil. The ichneumon and meerkat may stand opposite each other on their hind legs and then fall against each other and embracing with the front legs. An ichneumon may initiate fighting play by pushing sideways or attempting to mount the partner. The meerkat often bites its partner's fur and then violently shakes its head and executes flinging movements. The Indian mongoose will sometimes invite its keeper to play by biting his clothes and shaking them as if they were its prey.

The roles of attacker and defender are inter-changeable. During the changeover, ichneumons fight each other with their feet for a short time while they lie stretched out on the floor with their bellies towards each other. Or they may stand opposite each other with their bodies arched, whipping the floor with their tails. When fighting play is first initiated the reactions of the two ichneumons may be so similar that it is not easy to tell which is the attacker and which the defender (Dücker, 1965).

During play fighting some of the components of real defence may occur. For instance, the Indian mongoose and the meerkat may lie on their backs and lift the hind part of the body so far that the belly is protected. On further playful attack from the partner or by a human hand, the body may be turned around further so that it is almost a ball, and finally it may be standing on its hind legs with the open mouth presented to the attacker from one side of a leg or between the legs (figure 10A).

In play fighting with the human hand, the Indian mongoose clasps it very firmly with its front paws and engages in inhibited biting. It may then suddenly run away and as suddenly return to the attack. In all of these fighting games there is evidently a considerable degree of freedom: the sequences are often mixed so that attack may begin from a quite unexpected direction.

Fighting play may occur when the mongoose is alone. The meerkat and the Indian mongoose may lie on their back and bite the hind legs and tail, which seems to replace the missing partner. The meerkat and the ichneumon may also spin around chasing their own tail.

Flight and hiding play. Fighting play often switches over into flight and hiding play and then back again into fighting play. The very evident distinction between real flight or escape and play flight has already been noted. When two mongooses are playing, the role of pursuer and pursued often alternates, particularly when one animal has been pushed into a situation from which there is no escape. As might be expected, the chaser is usually more intensely engaged than the chased so that the animal being chased is usually the first to break off the game. Flight play frequently leads to hiding play in which one of the partners flees behind some object or into shelter of some kind, e.g. its sleeping box. It may then suddenly dart upon its pursuer from ambush and withdraw again very quickly. Sometimes, as has been noted in meerkats, both partners simultaneously hide and lie in wait until a pretence attack from one causes the other to flee.

Prey-catching play. This kind of play usually follows the general behaviour pattern of real prey-catching, but it is not so stereotyped. When real prey is used, the game cannot always be distinguished from real prey-catching except that serious attempts to kill are temporarily absent. However, play behaviour is easily enough recognised as such when the prey is a dummy of some kind. A large number of objects may substitute for the prey in prey-catching play, e.g. brushes, feathers, rags, balls of all kinds, nuts, bits of wood, and rubber rings.

The Indian mongoose, the ichneumon, and the meerkat play in a very similar manner with rolling objects or those that move when touched: they lie in wait for the dummy prey, run towards it, usually in a pattering gallop, seize the dummy between their teeth, and run about with it. The Indian mongoose and the ichneumon often fling away the dummy prey and then circle around it. They may scratch near it, jump forwards and backwards over it, and then drop on to it and crouch with the front paws on the dummy. Sometimes they spring up and simultaneously fling the object backwards between their legs (see p. 6).

Experimental games. The Indian mongoose and the ichneumon are very curious, and they tend to examine anything new in their environment immediately. Gluckman & Sroges (1966) examined the reactions of 48 kinds of carnivores to objects placed in their cages. Amongst these were two females and one male meerkat, which ranked 37th, 41st, and 46th respectively. It is difficult to avoid the conclusion that either their meerkats were abnormal in some way or the experiments were conducted improperly: the great curiosity of mongooses has been commented upon by very many of those who have had anything to do with them. Also, our own experiences with the Indian mongoose suggest that its curiosity is exceptionally well developed.

The highly developed curiosity behaviour of the Indian mongoose (Plate IX, facing p. 74) and the ichneumon contributes to the complexity of their games, which are more complex than those of the meerkat, in which play is generally less intense. Their experimental games have been described in some detail (summary in Dücker, 1965).

They invent unusual combinations of movements such as rolling in a tipped-over waste paper basket: the Indian mongoose, for instance, would often roll to and fro while lying on its back in the basket. All three liked to slip their heads into cardboard rolls or into paper bags and then run about thus blindfolded until they collided with some object. After a collision they would back out of the roll or paper bag and once more enter it and repeat the game, which has been appropriately called 'blind man's buff' by Rensch & Dücker. The female Indian mongoose and the meerkat would sometimes play a 'tortoise game': they would slip under various objects, such as basket-lids or pieces of paper, and then run about with these on their backs. They often play with their drinking bowls by turning them around again and again, or pushing them, or pulling them behind with their front paws.

Objects such as wooden balls, bits of wood, or food are sometimes carried in their mouths to a drinking bowl full of water. These are dropped into the water and then playfully moved about under water with the paws. They are then taken out with the mouth and paws and thrown into the water again. Once this game began, the objects would be thrown into the water and rescued several times in succession. The Indian mongoose also likes to grope under water. Dücker suggests that this is an innate action, which in nature serves to fish prey out of the water.

Hiding and fetching play objects can properly be included in the category of experimental games: hiding of prey or food was not otherwise observed by Dücker in the two species of *Herpestes*. A female Indian mongoose which we kept as a pet would often take its food, such as a pigeon, behind a board or into a pile of timber until it was entirely concealed and then eat it. But this behaviour is to be distinguished from hiding prey because the attempt to eat in a sheltered spot seems to be its only motivation. No mongoose has been observed to cover up or hide its prey in the way that many other kinds of carnivores do.

Another game was chasing a ball thrown by their keeper. After the ball stopped rolling, the mongoose would lie down beside it until the keeper threw it again. One Indian mongoose would retrieve the ball and return it to within about one metre of the thrower (Rensch & Dücker, 1959). A number of other activities, such as somersaulting, have been included amongst experimental games by Dücker. One of the characteristics of experimental games is that once 'invented' they are repeated frequently.

Sexual play. This kind of play is hard to distinguish from serious sexual behaviour. Individual components of sexual behaviour are occasionally introduced into genuine play sequences. For instance, in both the ichneumon and the meerkat mounting is often an invitation to a fighting game (Dücker, 1965). During pretence fighting the female Indian mongoose will often assume positions that are ordinarily used during genuine sexual behaviour (Dücker, 1965).

VIII
Language

ALL mammals and most other kinds of animals communicate with each other by means of sounds. Broadly speaking, the complexity of the language used increases as we pass on the one hand from solitary to gregarious and social species and on the other hand from primitive to relatively highly developed forms. Even amongst invertebrates a highly complex language may be evolved if they live in societies. For instance, we now know from the work of Wenner and others that sounds play a very important part in communication in the honeybee colony: no less than ten different sounds are involved in communication, and several of these have already been related to specific activities.

The language of the meerkat (*Suricata suricatta*) has been described by Dücker (1962) and Ewer (1963a), but no attempt has been made to analyse the language of any other mongoose. The frequencies of some of the sounds made by the meerkat and the banded mongoose are noted by Tembrock (1963). The meerkat makes most of its sounds with its mouth closed. The newborn young make small, bird-like cries practically all of the time that they are awake. Similar 'nest-chirping' is made by the young of other Viverridae such as genets and also by polecats, and martens. Two days after birth the young kept by Dücker made penetrating noises when the mother left the nest. She ignored this noise but would rush to protect the young when Dücker made other noises. For the first few days the young were very lively but there was not much difference between the sounds that they made. The nest-chirping became continuous when the mother left the nest.

After the young were four days old they made *kveer kveer* sounds if they wanted to drink. These changed to a purring sound if they were suckling or when they were held in the hand. The young of *Herpestes auropunctatus* also make a purring sound when they are suckling (Powell, 1913; Prater, 1935), although Baldwin *et al.*

(1952) say that their specimens of *auropunctatus* never made a sound that could be likened to purring. Powell says that the mature mother would purr whenever given a drink of milk but that he could not induce her to purr over any other kind of food.

Ewer comments on the interesting fact that no cry of pain is made by meerkats even when paws and tails have been trodden on or feet caught in a door. The adult male is normally much more silent than the female.

The sounds made by the meerkat are characteristic of certain situations, and, according to Ewer, may be classified as follows:

Aggressive or mixed threat. If an enemy such as a dog approaches it is threatened with growls. If it approaches sufficiently closely violent explosive spitting begins. These sounds are accompanied by postures and movements that appear to combine the conflicting tendencies to attack and to refrain from attacking. In encounters with other individuals of the same species growling is sometimes used when defending food against possible theft. Dücker found that spitting began on the 11th day after birth, and she thinks it was developed from the kind of squeaking noise they began to make on the 7th day while they were resting. She found that the first directed threatening move accompanied by a threatening noise took place on the 12th day, which is the day when the eyes are first distinctly open.

Defensive threat. This is a sharp and violent clucking noise that is rapidly repeated: it is '. . . a "cross noise" in any language.' That it is defensive in character is shown not only by the fact that while it is being made the meerkat shows little tendency to bite seriously but also by the fact that it is normally accompanied by the purely defensive 'belly up' posture. The sharp and violent clucking noise is produced if the meerkat is picked up against its will, by the mother if the young attempt to suckle her when she is not so inclined, or by an adult when it is disturbed by another. Ewer has not heard the noise made in a serious threat against a genuine enemy, but she thinks this is because she has never witnessed a genuine enemy press an attack to the point where the meerkat abandons offensive or mixed threatening behaviour and is forced to its last line of defence, which is the belly-up position.

Feeding. Little *wurruck-wurruck* sounds and grunts of satisfaction are made when they are feeding. Domestic cats learned the significance of these sounds made by the litter when eating and would quickly come to the scene to share the meal.

Danger warning. A clear drawn out note is used to express anxiety. When the intensity of the note is increased it becomes the fear note and serves as a warning cry. As danger approaches more closely, the cry is louder and is repeated more often. The danger warning can be subdivided according to whether the danger threatens from the air or on the ground. The cry for an aerial predator, such as a hawk, is a long drawn out and clear liquid *waauk-waauk.* For a ground predator the cry is more abrupt and gruffer. Ewer thinks that the reason for this is that there is always a tendency to attack where a ground predator is concerned, and the gruffness of the warning note reflects fear mixed with aggression. On the other hand, there is obviously no possibility of attacking a distant aerial predator such as a hawk, which is therefore not threatened, and so the hawk warning is an undiluted fear sound. Nevertheless, Ewer once heard a mother growl at a hawk. The mother was in the garden with her young. When the hawk appeared, the young gathered close behind the mother in response to her warning, and the mother then looked up at the hawk and growled.

Generalised alarm barking. A general and unspecific kind of defiance is expressed by repeated short and sharp barks. The adults almost always use this kind of barking in response to certain auditory stimuli, when another individual makes the violent clucking defensive noise or when dogs in the neighbourhood are barking. The young use a rather similar yelping bark after they have left the nest as a distress call if one is left alone. It is not certain whether in the field the barking of one adult will cause another to follow suit. Unnatural noises may evoke alarm barking, for instance the sound of a typewriter or an egg beater. On one occasion the alarm barking was provoked by visual stimuli: the mother was on a window sill and saw a dog enter the garden. This caused her to return to her young while giving the alarm call very loudly, but after a brief burst of alarm barking she settled down.

It is characteristic of alarm barking that it is not usually directed towards the source of the sound but is directed 'outwards'. For instance, a meerkat sitting on the desk beside the typewriter that is evoking its barking may bark towards the window. In the field it seems likely that alarm barking serves as a general alert call to the whole colony and that if one starts barking the others will follow suit just as with dogs.

Settling down. When the female is settling down to sleep she often makes a '. . . clear plaintive cry, repeated with marked diminuendo and gradually fading out'.

Dissatisfaction. A low crow-like cawing is made by the male when he is dissatisfied. 'Frequently this cry is used as a signal to a human companion indicating that action should be taken to set things right: for instance, he will sit at one's feet crowing as a sign that one is in a position making it impossible for him to climb on one's lap.' The female has not been heard to make this sound, and it may be a new sound that has been produced as a result of the unusual relationship with human companions.

IX
Colour vision

APART from a little work on colour vision, hardly anything is known of the sense organs of mongooses. Colour perception is on the whole less well developed in mammals than in any other group of vertebrates. This is undoubtedly directly related to the fact that most are nocturnal, and the capacity to distinguish between colours has very little selective value for a nocturnal animal. Colour-blind animals of course distinguish differences in the intensity of reflected light, but are insensitive to differences in colour. When colour perception is evolved, a whole new dimension is added to the qualities of objects: it now becomes possible to distinguish between things that reflect light of equal intensity but of different wave length, that is, colour.

Two kinds of units are present in the retina of most vertebrate eyes: (1) colour-sensitive cells called cones, and (2) rods that do not mediate responses to differences in colour but have a very low light intensity threshold. This means that by simply examining the structure of the eye we can say something about its capacities. For instance, an animal with only rods in the retina is colour blind, whereas one that also has some cones is probably capable of at least some colour discrimination. The absence of cones in colour-blind vertebrates is probably due to a secondary loss, whereas the presence of a large number of cones may be primitive or secondary. The structure of the retina of *H. edwardsi* and *H. ichneumon* has been described by Dücker (1959).

A commonly accepted theory of colour vision has it that there are different kinds of cones, or colour modulators, each with its own photosensitive pigment and therefore its own characteristic spectral sensitivity curve. For instance, Granit distinguishes between blue-, green-, and red-modulators. With modern electro-physiological techniques it is possible to record action potentials from single cells and so apparently prove the existence or otherwise of colour vision.

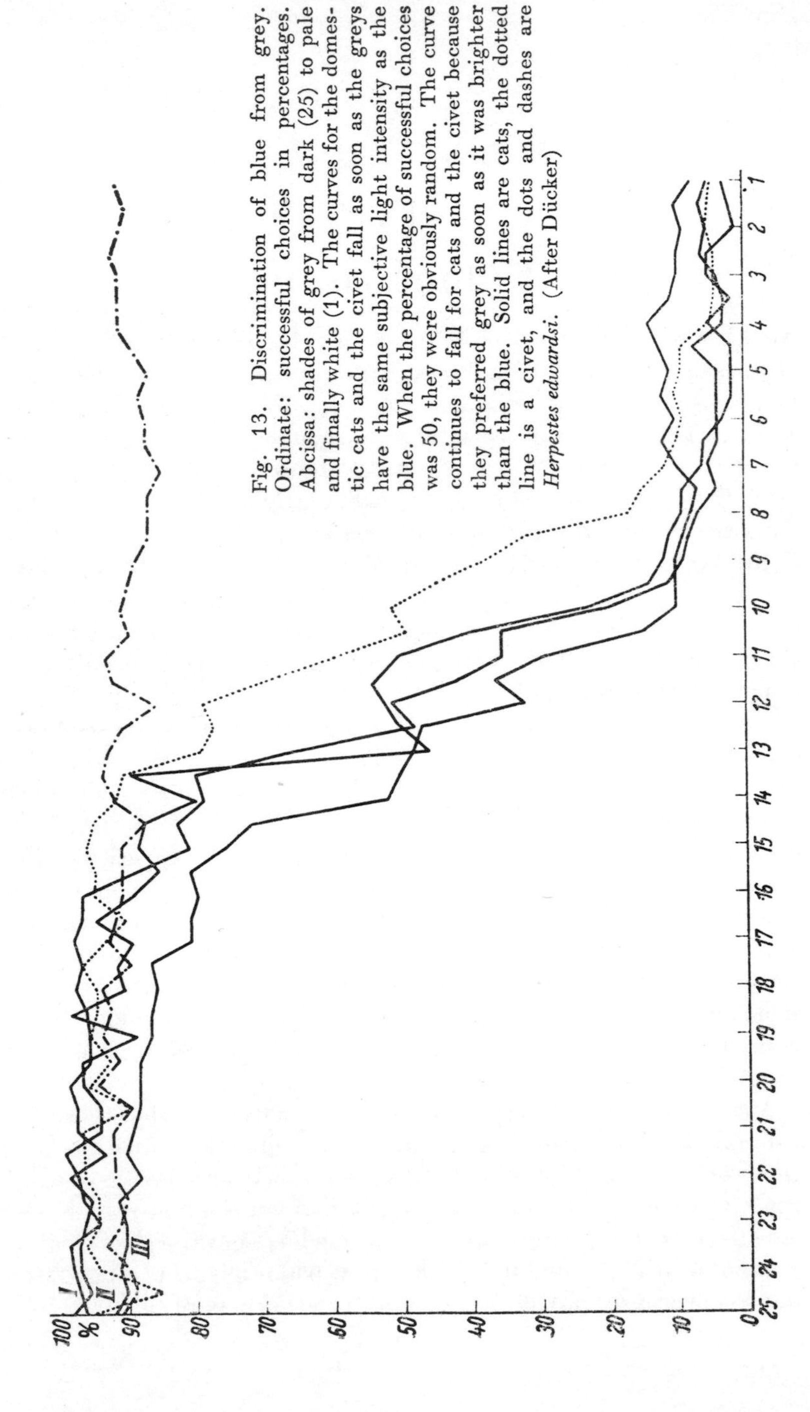

Fig. 13. Discrimination of blue from grey. Ordinate: successful choices in percentages. Abcissa: shades of grey from dark (25) to pale and finally white (1). The curves for the domestic cats and the civet fall as soon as the greys have the same subjective light intensity as the blue. When the percentage of successful choices was 50, they were obviously random. The curve continues to fall for cats and the civet because they preferred grey as soon as it was brighter than the blue. Solid lines are cats, the dotted line is a civet, and the dots and dashes are *Herpestes edwardsi*. (After Dücker)

However, the demonstration of a selective action by certain wave lengths does not mean that the brain is capable of a real distinction between colours, final proof of which can be had from animals only by training experiments: the cones and their photosensitive pigments only provide data which still has to be processed by the brain. Thus, although some electro-physiologists claim that the domestic cat has colour vision, careful experiments of the type described below show that it has not.

By training methods Dücker (1957, 1964) was able to show that *Herpestes edwardsi* could distinguish certain colours. The animals are presented with a choice of food containers with differently coloured lids. One container is empty and the other has food. The wooden lids are lined with paper of the required colour. In order to avoid providing secondary clues, such as differences in odour or surface structure, the papers were coated with a layer of wax (experimenters often overrate the impermeability of a layer of wax to small molecules).

The mongoose is first trained to distinguish a colour and a shade of grey. In order to eliminate discrimination based on differences in light intensity, it is necessary to show that the animal can distinguish colour from a large number of shades of grey, that is, 30 to 60 shades. Only when the mongoose was able to distinguish the colour from all shades of grey, including those that were the same intensity as the colour, was it assumed that colour vision existed. In one series of experiments, for instance, the mongoose was first trained to distinguish a particular colour from black. A mongoose learned to distinguish green from black after 500 trials. Black was then replaced by a large number of shades of grey ranging from dark grey to almost white and finally to white. Each shade of grey was presented 50 times, and if a correct choice was made at least 80 per cent of the times, it was assumed that the mongoose had mastered the difference.

In experiments of the type described above, it was found that *H. edwardsi* could distinguish the four primary colours (blue, green, yellow, red) from grey. It could also distinguish orange and violet from all shades of grey, even from those of equal intensity. However, when offered a choice of colour only, it had difficulty in distinguishing between red and violet, red and orange, green and blue, and violet and blue. In contrast to the mongoose, genets, and domestic cats (Fig. 13) were colour blind, and the civet (*Viverricula malaccensis*) was blind to yellow and blue but not to red and green.

This is not perhaps a surprising result in view of the fact that *H. edwardsi* is very much more of a diurnal animal than the other carnivores tested. Great differences in the capacity for colour vision are likely to be found when strictly diurnal mongooses are compared with those that are usually nocturnal.

X

In the West Indies

THE small Indian mongoose, *Herpestes auropunctatus*, was first introduced into the West Indies in the 1870s for the purpose of controlling rats in sugar cane plantations. Its introduction into this region was to prove one of the most disastrous attempts ever made at biological control. In both its timing and thoughtlessness it ranks with the activities of a certain Mr Bieckert who in 1872 and 1873 liberated 20 cages of sparrows in the Argentine to control the moth *Oiketicus kirbyi* Guild. Lahille & Joan (1926) bitterly remark that the sparrows ate what the moth left.

Mammals have rarely been used for biological control, which is surprising in view of the large numbers that have been successfully established in new countries either for hunting, like the European red fox in Australia, or for fur, like the North American muskrat in Europe and Asia.

Apart from mongooses, so few mammals have been introduced into other countries for biological control that they may all be noted. The stoat, ferret, and weasel were introduced from Europe into Australia for controlling rabbits and in 1885 and 1886 into New Zealand for the same purpose. Stoats and weasels from Holland were introduced into Terschelling island in 1931 for rat control. The kinkajou from northern South America was established on Juan Fernandez island off Chile for rat control. The masked shrew, *Sorex cinereus* Kerr, feeds on the cocoons of the larch sawfly. It was introduced into Newfoundland from New Brunswick in 1958. By 1964 it was clear that the shrew was spreading rapidly on the island and playing an increasing part in the control of the sawfly.

SOME PRINCIPLES OF BIOLOGICAL CONTROL

Before describing the way in which the mongoose has been used for biological control in this and the following chapter, some of the general principles underlying this kind of control should be noted, and we may begin by defining what is meant by a pest.

A species is not regarded as a pest until its population density sometimes or frequently fluctuates above a level at which damage of economic significance occurs. The problem of its economic control may therefore be stated in very general terms as the problem of depressing its population density sufficiently for it to fluctuate below a level at which damage of economic significance occurs. When the problem is defined in this way, it becomes evident that it is necessary to know something about the factors that in nature determine that no one species multiplies unhindered and that its populations are not reduced to the point of extinction.

The factors that determine population densities in nature are of two kinds, density-independent and density-dependent. By density-independent factors is meant those that affect the species irrespective of the density of its population. Climate is usually the most important density-independent factor. Quality and quantity of food, as well as chemicals used in controlling pests, are other density-independent factors. Density-dependent factors, on the other hand, are those the effect of which depends upon the population density of the species. Intraspecific competition and predators, parasites, and pathogens are density-dependent factors. Of these, intraspecific competition is the only density-dependent factor that is affected solely by numbers: density-dependent factors such as parasites and predators cannot be expected to show an unfailingly exact response to changes in the population densities of their hosts for they have environmental relations that are quite independent of their hosts.

The population density of each species fluctuates within limits imposed by the total density-independent environment, but within these limits density fluctuations are dampened by density-dependent factors. Contrary to a rather popular view, however, only rarely is the combined effect of density-independent and density-dependent factors so benign as to permit any significant degree of intraspecific competition (Hinton, 1957).

Most of the effort expended on biological control concerns the use of insects against each other or against weeds. However, viruses, bacteria, fungi, and other organisms are also fairly often used to control insect or plant pests.

When the introduction of a foreign animal results in preventing the population density of a pest from ever rising to a level at which damage of economic significance occurs, the operation is described as completely successful, providing only that the introduced animal does no significant damage on its own account. If, however, the introduced animal only depresses the population density of the pest so that its depredations are not as severe as before, the operation is only partially successful. In both the West Indies and the Hawaiian islands the mongoose not only did significant damage on its own account—raids on poultry and so on—but at best only partially depressed the populations of rats. Thus on none of the islands of either region was it a complete success, and on many it became itself a serious pest doing far more harm than good in the way of killing rats.

To use animals against each other has its own appeal and may be startlingly successful. A single operation, such as that of introducing a foreign animal, may effect a lasting cure. Thus biological control requires an effort that is non-repetitive or at least potentially non-repetitive. In sharp contrast to this, chemical control is by its very nature repetitive. Chemicals do not kill all of the individuals of a pest, and they do not persist. Of course, in certain very special circumstances it may be possible to kill all individuals of an established pest in a particular area with a chemical, but exceptions of this kind are so infrequent as not to affect the general problem. Furthermore, even in such an instance, if control is to be anything but temporary constant vigilance must be maintained against the introduction of the pest from another area.

As we have seen, by biological control is meant the use of one living organism against another in such a way that the exercise is non-repetitive or at least potentially non-repetitive. The manner in which insects and, more especially, viruses and micro-organisms are sometimes used against pests does not constitute biological control in any sense except that biological material is being used. For instance, the way in which viruses and bacteria are used against the alfalfa caterpillar in California does not differ *in principle* from the way in which DDT or some other chemical might be used against the caterpillar: *Bacillus thuringiensis* Berl. and a polyhedral virus are established in the area. Natural outbreaks of the *Bacillus* and the virus do not occur regularly enough to give satisfactory economic control. Both are produced in the laboratory and sprayed or dusted on the lucerne fields each year. The production and use of these, or any other organisms, in a necessarily repetitive way can only be justified if they be as effective as the same amount of human labour of comparable skill spent in manufacturing and using some chemical.

Both potentially non-repetitive and necessarily repetitive methods of control that make use of living organisms are commonly included in the term biological control. But to do so inevitably means that an ineffectual antithesis is drawn between the two: the form of the activity is confounded with its content of practical significance (Hinton, 1957).

INTRODUCTION INTO THE CARIBBEAN ISLANDS

Before we consider the effects of the introduction of the mongoose in the West Indies,* a little may be said about the earlier attempts to control rats on these islands by means of other animals.

The black rat was already a serious pest on the French islands by 1654 (Du Tertre, 1654). In 1789 it was estimated that it often destroyed a quarter or more of the Jamaican cane crop (Allen, 1911). The first attempt to control the rats by biological means, other than the use of dogs, was apparently the introduction of ferrets from Europe. These were alleged to have been incapacitated by the attacks of chigoes or burrowing fleas. No member of the weasel family has ever been successfully established in the West Indies. Then in about 1750 Sir Charles Price tried to establish a South American carnivore in Jamaica. One of Gosse's (1851) correspondents interviewed a descendant of Sir Charles who '. . . informed me that, according to family tradition, the animal introduced by his ancestor was a substitute for the ferret. It had been found that European Ferrets were useless by their inability to overcome the Chigoe infestment of the colony. Sir Charles Price bethought him that if he could find an animal in the country of the Chigoe, corresponding to the weasel of Europe, he would accomplish the naturalisation of a Rat-destroyer with instincts capable of counteracting the plague of the parasitical insect. He accordingly procured something from South America, that in the eyes of the negroes had strong rat characteristics, but which was no Rat. It was of large size. Several were set at large about the house at the Decoy, in St Mary's, and at Worthy Park, to establish themselves as they might. The identity of the animal introduced by Sir Charles has never been established. The negroes were impressed with something rat-like in their appearance and called them "Charley Price Rats".'

Two further attempts to control rats in Jamaica by means of other

* Besides the papers cited later in the text, many others contain notes on the mongoose in the Caribbean, e.g. Anon. (1818b, c), Beebe (1922), Lewis (1942, 1945, 1953), Roth (1943), Schwarz (1943), Urich (1914).

animals were made before the introduction of the mongoose. In 1762 Thomas Raffles imported an ant, *Formica omnivora* from Cuba. This species became known locally as the 'Tom Raffle ant'. Writing 120 years later, Morris (1882) says that the ant '. . . has remained, to this day, a firm friend to the Sugar planter, and a foe to all pests of rats and vermin.' The identity of the Raffle ant is not known (Wheeler *in* Réaumur, 1926). In 1844 the giant toad, *Bufo marinus*, was introduced by Antony Davis from Barbados. This toad had previously been introduced from Cayenne into Martinique and then from Martinique into Barbados. Although the toad will eat young and half grown rats, it probably never played a significant part in their control.

There were a number of early and unsuccessful attempts to introduce the mongoose into one or other of the islands. It is often said (e.g. Myers, 1931b) that it was first successfully established in Trinidad about 1870. However, we have been unable to discover any convincing account of its first introduction into Trinidad, and it is possible that it was introduced into this island from Jamaica shortly after 1872.

Before 1872 at least six different people tried unsuccessfully to establish the mongoose in Jamaica. Their names and addresses are given by Morris (1882). Most if not all of the animals were imported from London and had been bred in captivity, and they were '. . . literally afraid of a rat.' However this may be, the first successful attempt was made by W. B. Espeut, to whom the idea of importing the mongoose from India was first suggested to him by his wife (Espeut, 1882). On 13th February 1872, by the East Indian ship *Merchantman* he received 9 mongooses from Calcutta, 4 males and 5 females for which he paid 9 pounds in '. . . reimbursement of cost attending the procuring and transmitting.' Within six months there was evidence clear and certain that rats were much less destructive than had ever been known. Within three years neighbouring estates had found a similar benefit. Planters began to buy all they could. Natives trapped them and sold them at five shillings to a pound each. The mongoose spread to all parts of the island, and a decade later was said to effect a saving of about £150,000 a year. Amongst the natives the mongoose was often referred to as 'Massa Espeut Ratta'.

Espeut claims to have sent the mongoose to Cuba, Puerto Rico, Grenada, and Barbados before 1882. However, Barbour (1930) says it was not established in Cuba until about 1886. It spread very slowly in Cuba, and by 1929 did not occupy more than about 1000 square miles about Havana. In Puerto Rico it is said to have been established about 1877 (Colon, 1930; Palmer, 1898), in Barbados between 1877 and 1879, and in Hispanola it was certainly established before 1895 (Allen, 1911).

The mongoose was introduced into St Croix from Jamaica in 1884 (letter in the *St Croix Avis*, 20 February 1884). It soon became very numerous and reduced the number of rats, which, however, remained too high. Public opinion in the Virgin Islands became divided on the value of the mongoose for rodent control, particularly because of its destruction of poultry and ground-nesting game birds as well as beneficial reptiles. The Territorial Government in due course authorised payment of a bounty, 10 cents for males and 15 cents for females. In the 10 years from 1940 to 1950 bounty payments were made on about 7000 mongooses.*

Federal aid (USA) was given to the local authorities in 1941 to assist in restoration of wildlife on the Virgin Islands. Somewhat later the futility of trying to introduce quail (*Colinus virginanus*) so long as there were many mongooses was realised. The mongoose ate the eggs and young and was able to stalk and kill the adults. In his report for the 'Mongoose Control Project', Spencer (1950) recommends a programme of poisoning. He also suggests that the inhabitants should begin to eat the mongoose, the flesh of which he says is very appetizing and like that of rabbit or squirrel in appearance. He suggests that hunting the mongoose should be taken up for sport, the advantage being that, 'While approaching the bait the animals became so attentive to the lure that a hunter could get in several shots if need be.'

The mongoose was introduced from Barbados into Surinam in 1900 (Husson, 1960). Suffice it to say here that its present distribution in the Caribbean, summarised on p. 116 and discussed at some length by a number of writers (e.g. Barbour, 1930; Myers, 1931a, 1931b; Westermann, 1953), had been achieved by 1900. By this time most local governments had passed regulations prohibiting its importation.

Two unsuccessful attempts were made to introduce the mongoose into Dominica (Barbour, 1930). The first was made in the 1880s, but the mongooses died in transit. On the second attempt ten were

* During this same period the price in England of a semi-tame mongoose of any species varied from several pounds to as much as £20, according to the dealer.

set at large in northern Dominica, but they did not survive. Some think they were caught by the local boa, others that the climate was unsuitable. Dominica is the wettest place in the West Indies. Further attempts to introduce the mongoose into this island were prohibited by law.

In the 1890s there were several reports to the effect that mongooses, particularly in Jamaica, were becoming less numerous because of the attacks of ticks which had increased greatly in number (e.g. Anon., 1897b; Cousins *in* Anon., 1918a). The supposed increase in ticks was attributed by some to the fact that the mongoose destroyed so many of the lizards and toads that had formerly kept the ticks in check (Howard, 1897). These views were not founded on sufficient evidence (Anon., 1897a) and were soon discarded by most.

In most of the islands about ten to fifteen years after its introduction there was a complete change of public opinion. Rats were still numerous, and the mongoose not only destroyed birds and useful reptiles and toads, but it became notorious for its destruction of poultry. In Jamaica, where the damage by rats in cane fields was particularly severe, this phase of public disfavour soon passed, and the mongoose is still considered to do more good than harm.

The kind of arguments used for and against the mongoose may be illustrated by the following quotations from letters and reports compiled by Anon. (1918a). Mosse and Craig say of the mongoose in Jamaica, 'We find that although the rat has to a great extent disappeared in the fields he is almost if not quite as numerous as he was prior to the introduction of the Mongoose, and quite as destructive elsewhere than in the field. It would appear that the sagacity of the rat enables him to outwit his enemy by concealing himself in trees and houses during the day when the Mongoose is abroad, and descending to forage at nights when the Mongoose has retired, and thus by accommodating himself to the habits of the imported animal he increases and commits his depredations practically unmolested except in the fields . . . Of the numerous strong complaints made against him the most serious at present (1890), seems to us to be the enormous destruction of poultry. It was stated by many witnesses that whereas formerly the raising of poultry was both easy and profitable it is now next to impossible, except under elaborate and costly protective measures to rear poultry of any kind. Hence it is that a great source of income to the peasantry of ordinary working people and of very poor persons, particularly poor females, has been destroyed. The price of poultry has also in consequence greatly increased, they are extremely scarce in most parts of the country, and the people are so discouraged that in many districts they have practically abandoned an industry which until the mongoose appeared was most profitable' (his syntax). A contrary view is expressed by Fawcett and Plaxton who say, 'We do not feel assured that the benefit done by the Mongoose has been more than counterbalanced by serious injury . . . There is also evidence that the coffee cultivator has benefited and it is fair to suppose that when the Mongoose is in force the damage done by the rat is minimised. What is lost in poultry is gained in coffee, corn, chocolate and other crops.' Barcaly says, 'The rat is a far greater pest and a more costly pest (in 1917) than ever the mongoose has been in Jamaica . . . Before the mongoose were introduced here, there were large sugar estates paying over £400 per annum for rat catching alone, but a few years after the introduction of the mongoose, these estates had practically no damage done to their sugar canes. With the extension of the cultivation of bananas and cocoa, however, the rats have become largely arboreal and can travel along the interlocked branches of the cocoa, while their nests are often in the branches of cocoa . . . If the mongoose was non-existent, the rat would again take to the ground and would probably become as common and costly to field crops as it was before.'

In a 1911 report of a commission established to determine what action should be taken in Barbados it is stated (Anon., 1918a) that, 'We, therefore, consider that no good can result from the proposed examination of the stomachs of one hundred mongooses, especially of those of mongooses from the districts in which there has been an increase in the number of rat eaten canes, as this would further reduce their numbers where they were badly wanted . . . We are of the opinion that the benefit to the cane crop derived from the presence of the mongoose is so great that a stop should at once be put to their destruction, and we, therefore, recommend that the Mongoose Destruction Act of 1904 be repealed.'

In Martinique and St Lucia the mongoose was introduced, or so it is said, to control the fer-de-lance snake, once exceedingly common and now much rarer. In these two islands, as in Jamaica, the mongoose is supposed to do more good than harm (Myers, 1931b). Its larger relative, *H. edwardsi*, was introduced in 1910 from India into some of the Japanese islands such as Ryukyu and Tonaki. Here it is said (Takashima, 1954) to have been of no small service in exterminating the pit viper, *Trimeresurus flavoviridis* (Hallowell). In the 1960s *H. ichneumon* was introduced into Italy to see if it would help control vipers (e.g. Bruijns, 1961).

On most of the other islands the mongoose is considered to be an unmitigated pest. Bounties for its destruction have been paid by the Governments of Trinidad, St Kitts, Antigua, Barbados, and St Vincent. In some islands it became necessary to pass an ordinance making it illegal to keep mongooses in captivity because it was feared that they were being bred for the reward. In a minute by the Chief Inspector of the Leeward Islands Police Force of 12th October 1917 it is stated (Anon., 1918a) that, 'The bodies of the Mongoose are brought to any Police Station. The sex is then determined and the body decapitated to prevent fraud by a second presentation of the same body. The bodies and heads are afterwards buried in lime.' In Trinidad during the first eight months of 1930, 21,231 mongooses were paid for, the corresponding figures for 1928 and 1929 being 30,026 and 32,650 respectively (Myers, 1931b).

It is of interest to recall that before the danger of introducing mongooses was known, Espeut (1882) said, '. . . and I marvel that Australia and New Zealand do not obtain this useful animal in order to destroy the plague of Rabbits in those countries.' Shortly after this, however, a mongoose was introduced from Ceylon into North Queensland to cope with the plague of rats that threatened the sugar planters (Anon., 1946). Numbers were set free in the cane fields. All disappeared with the exception of one which had evidently been reared as a pet and soon established itself as a member of the nearest household. The species of mongoose that was introduced into Queensland is not now known, but it was probably *Herpestes edwardsi* or *H. smithi*.

EFFECTS ON THE LOCAL FAUNA

Reptiles

None of those who have made a study of the mongoose in the West Indies doubt that it has more or less seriously affected the numbers of certain species of reptiles, birds, and other animals. Although it is often said that this or that species of reptile or bird was exterminated by the mongoose, in no instance that we know of is there certain proof of this. Furthermore, it is always well to remember that what is really meant by such a statement is only that the mongoose *together* with already existing hazards—parasites, predators, and adverse physical conditions—resulted in the extermination of the reptile or bird. Because these other hazards are never absent, it is never possible in a strict sense to speak of one species by itself exterminating another. In the following paragraphs some of the more notable effects of the mongoose upon the fauna of the West Indies are summarised.

It has for long been recognized that ground lizards of the genus *Ameiva* were particularly important in destroying insect pests in the West Indies (e.g. Wolcott, 1924). These and other useful reptiles have been greatly reduced in numbers or even made extinct on many of the islands on which the mongoose was established.* The green turtle (*Chelonia mydas*), a table delicacy of wide repute, may also be seriously affected. It comes ashore only to lay, and the mongoose digs out the eggs (Seaman & Randall, 1962). As noted elsewhere (p. 16), in Trinidad and St Lucia boas prey on the mongoose and are thought to keep down its numbers to some extent.

Birds

It is difficult to assess with any confidence the effect of the mongoose on the birds of the islands. Barbour (1930) says that ground-nesting birds are either extirpated or they learn to change their habits. Allen (1911) could find no trace of the pea dove (*Engyptila wellsi*) on Grenada during his stay in 1910, and by 1905 the moun-

* According to Barbour (1930), by 1929 the following lizards and harmless or useful snakes had been seriously affected by the mongoose. LIZARDS. *Ameiva prolops* Cope: Extinct on St Croix; small colonies exist on neighbouring Protestant Cay and Green Cay where the mongoose does not occur (Seaman & Randall, 1962). *A. exsul* (Cope): Extinct on St Thomas; very common on Culebra where the mongoose is absent (Schmidt, 1928). *A. aquilinia* Garman: Extinct on St Vincent. *Mabuya sloanii* (Dardin): Extinct on St Thomas and St Croix; very rare or extinct on Puerto Rico. *M. mabouia* (D. and B.): Extinct on Martinique. *M. luciae* Garman: Extinct on St Lucia. *M. aenea* Gray: Extinct on St Vincent and Grenada; rare on Trinidad. *M. lanceolata* Cope: Extinct on Barbados. *Gymnophthalmus pleii* Boucourt: Extinct on Martinique and St Lucia. SNAKES. *Alsophis rufiventris* (D. and B.): Extinct on St Kitts and Nevis; common on Saba and St Eustatius where the mongoose does not occur. *A. antillensis* (Schl.): Extinct on St Thomas. *A. sanctae-crucis* Cope: Extinct on St Croix. *A. leucomelas* (D. and B): Extinct on Guadeloupe and Marie Galante. *Drymobius boddaerti* (Sentzen): Extinct on St Vincent; very rare in Grenada. *Leimadophis exiguus* Cope: Extinct on St Thomas. *L. cursor* (Lacepide): Extinct on Martinique. *L. boulengeri* Barbour: Extinct on St Lucia. *L. perfuscus* (Cope): Extinct on Barbados. *L. melanotus* (Shaw): Extinct on Grenada; still common on Trinidad and on the mainland.

tain dove (*Geotrygon montana*) was extinct on St Vincent and had become very rare on Grenada (Clark, 1905). The mongoose is said to be the probable cause of the extinction or near extinction at one time of the quail dove (*Oreopeleia mystacea*) on St Croix (Seaman, 1952), although its numbers later increased considerably. Seaman says that a lot of the blame for the destruction of birds that has been shouldered by the mongoose may eventually prove to be due to the arboreal black rat. On the other hand, Williams (1918) points out that on Trinidad the commonest birds on the sugar estates are the ground doves, *Engyptila rufaxilla* and *E. verreauxi*, and the small black finch or cici-zebe, *Volatina jacarina*, all of which nest on or near the ground. Urich (1931) also says that, so far as his observations go, no species of bird has been exterminated on Trinidad. He says that the Trinidad possum (*Didelphys marsupialis*) has been established on most of the British islands of the Lesser Antilles and has, '. . . probably played a part in the decrease or even extinction of certain birds, notably the ground dove, *Geotrygon mystacea*.'

Seaman & Randall (1962) saw a mongoose attempting to steal an egg from beneath a pelican sitting on its nest on the top of a high tree on Buck Island. They point out that the frigate bird roosts on the island but does not nest there, whereas on other islets on which the mongoose is absent, such as Tobago in the British Virgin Islands, there are large nesting colonies.

Mammals

The mongoose kills the young of the Virginia or white-tailed deer (*Odocoileus virginianus*), a species introduced into St Croix about 1790 (Seaman & Randall, 1962). It will attack and kill fawns several days old and more than twice its own weight ($1\frac{1}{2}$ lb). Its larger relative, *H. edwardsi*, is accused of similar habits. It was introduced into Mauritius from India in the last century, and it is said to be partly responsible for the near extinction of Sambar deer introduced into the island from Batavia in 1939 (Maingard, 1954). In 1910 Allen (1911) found that the agouti was nearly extinct on Grenada because, or so he was told, its young were killed by the mongoose. It has been reported that on some of the islands young pigs, lambs, kittens, and even newly dropped calves are sometimes killed by the mongoose.

RABIES

During the last two decades the mongoose has attracted considerable attention as a reservoir and vector of the virus of canine rabies. The virus multiplies in the brain and central nervous system of mammals. The incubation period is usually two to four months. Some ten to twelve days before the death of the infected animal, the virus is found abundantly in the vascular system and also in the saliva. At this time the animal becomes capable of transmitting the disease and begins to show the outward symptons of rabies or hydrophobia. The disease is always fatal to the animal. When a human is bitten by an animal suspected of rabies, advantage can be taken of the long incubation period. The animal is kept for ten or twelve days. If it is alive and well at the end of this time, the person need take no precautions. If the animal is found to have rabies, a prolonged and painful course of injections of immune serum prepared from a horse is necessary, together with a vaccine made from the dead virus usually extracted from an infected rabbit. If no treatment is given death is certain. Rabies has been eliminated from some parts of the world by killing all infected animals and enforcing a strict quarantine against introduced ones. Rabies has not been endemic in England since before the first world war.

Rabies is present on many of the West Indian islands, but apparently not on the Virgin islands (Spencer, 1950; Seaman, 1952). In Puerto Rico, according to Tierkel *et al.* (1952), there were only twenty-one cases of rabies from 1911 to 1933 in dogs and farm animals. From 1933 to 1950 the island was considered to be one of the few rabies-free areas in the world, but in 1950 it was found that the mongoose was an important reservoir and vector of rabies. This was apparently the first time that rabies had been reported in a species of *Herpestes*, although at the end of last century the inhabitants of Barbados dreaded the bite of the mongoose because they thought it brought on rabies (Feilden, 1890). Taylor (1965) says that the mongoose is of the greatest importance as a carrier of rabies on Grenada, 'The number of cases of human infection with the disease through the bite of a mongoose is few but there have been numerous reports of domestic animals (donkeys and cattle) being bitten and subsequently dying of rabies-like symptoms.' The mongoose is sometimes a vector of rabies in other parts of the world. For instance, in South Africa the yellow mongoose, *Cynictis* (Plate X, facing p. 75) has been recognised as a vector of the disease since 1928 (Syman, 1940). In East Africa the slender mongoose, *Herpestes sanguineus*, is said to be very prone to rabies (Maberly, 1960).

Plate IX. A pet Indian mongoose. (TOP) Trying to investigate an object suspended on the washing line above it. (BOTTOM) Digging out the bowl of a pipe, which this mongoose could hardly ever resist doing although it was probably slightly burnt occasionally.

Plate X. The yellow mongoose, a vector of rabies in South Africa.

CONTROL

We are not here concerned with the control of the mongoose, but in the West Indies and the Hawaiian Islands control measures are sometimes necessary. The efficacy of bounty payments has been discussed by many. Methods of poisoning are described by Pimental (1955b), Seaman (1952), Spencer (1950), and Taylor (1965). So far as the Hawaiian Islands are concerned, Dotty (1945) has described poisoning methods in some detail. No doubt others will be as distressed as we are to think of poisoning so attractive an animal.

XI
In the Hawaiian Islands

THE Hawaiian Islands are volcanic, and most were formed less than 26 million years ago. The endemic fauna and flora is derived from forms that managed to survive transportation in the air or in the sea across immense stretches of the Pacific. The main or windward group consists of eight islands, and these are the only ones that concern us here. They are from the largest to the smallest: Hawaii, Maui, Oahu, Kauai, Molokai, Lanai, Niihau, and Kahoolwe.

Herpestes auropunctatus was imported from Jamaica in 1883 and liberated on Hawaii, Maui, and Oahu to control rats in sugar cane plantations. At some later date it was introduced into Molokai. The plantation owners of Kauai, Lanai, and Niihau oppose its introduction into these islands.

The climate of the Hawaiian Islands is well suited to the mongoose and is less extreme than that of the areas it occupies in continental India. It is found from sea level to as high as 10,000 feet on the islands of Maui and Hawaii, but most occur below 2000 feet. It favours areas with a warm and humid climate, mixed natural vegetation, and an adequate supply of ready-made retreats such as stone walls, boulders, or tangled underbrush. When adequate cover is available they may frequent the sea shore. At Pearl Harbor, for instance, they live on a small peninsula that juts out into the estuary. Here they feed on crabs which they dig out of their burrows in the sand as well as on both crabs and fish caught when stranded in shallow water in the tide pools.

The mongoose is the only important natural enemy of the rat in the Hawaiian Islands. In 1924 Pemberton (1925) collected 356 mongoose pellets in cane fields in Honokaa, Hawaii. A total of 88 per cent contained parts of rodents, including bones, teeth, and hair. Of these 52 per cent contained nothing but rodent parts, 36 per cent contained rodent and insect parts. The remaining 11 per cent contained nothing but bits of insects. Many of the owners of sugar cane plantations claim that the mongoose does more good than harm because he rids many areas of rats and insects. Pemberton says, '. . . it plays a certain definite part as a control factor. Being much less prolific than rodents it does not keep up with them sufficiently to be a "cure-all" for rats, but it helps.'

On Kauai there are no mongooses, and '. . . it may be more than a mere coincidence that the Norway rat has always been the dominant rat on that island' (Dotty, 1945). The uniformly higher rat damage in 1927 and 1928 on Kaui was blamed on the absence of the mongoose (Barnum, 1930), and it is now generally conceded that rat troubles on the Kauai plantations were consistently more acute and widespread than on other islands until effective poison baiting was used in 1938. Before 1939-40, rats on the windward side of Kauai took 25 to 30 per cent of the crop over whole fields and as much as 80 to 90 per cent of the cane was cut down by rats in limited areas at the head of gulches or next to forest waste land (Dotty, 1945).

Mongooses do not appear to suffer if they eat rats poisoned with zinc phosphide, but since the adoption of the system of baiting followed by thallium poisoning the slaughter of the mongoose has been terrific. As Dotty (1945) says, 'It is an unfortunate byproduct of our poison campaign that this most aggressive natural enemy of the rat should suffer so seriously.'

It has been said that in both the Hawaiian Islands (Walker, 1948) and in the West Indies (Barbour, 1930) the mongoose has caused some species of rats, such as the black rat, to nest in trees. It is thus claimed that by driving some kinds of rats up into the trees the mongoose has increased the damage that birds suffer from rats. Myers (1931) thinks that the brown rat would have driven the black up into the trees mongoose or no mongoose. He points out that in New Zealand, where there are no mongooses, the black rat became almost wholly arboreal following the introduction of its arch-competitor, the brown rat, which is now the domestic rat. In the Hawaiian Islands the black rat is an arboreal species as compared with the brown rat both in the islands with and those without the mongoose.

Four kinds of rats are found in the Hawaiian Islands:

1. The Polynesian rat, *Rattus hawaiiensis* Stone.
2. The brown, Norway, sewer, or wharf rat, *Rattus norvegicus* (Erxleben).

3. The black, house, or roof rat, *Rattus rattus rattus* (L.).
4. The Alexandrine rat, *Rattus rattus alexandrinus* (Geoffroy).

The Polynesian rat is derived from stock that perhaps entered the islands in prehistoric times. It is a small rat that burrows in the ground, often in the banks of streams or reservoirs. It is now to some extent supplanted by the three cosmopolitan species which arrived on the islands in sailing vessels, probably in the early part of the nineteenth century.

The brown rat is the most pugnacious of the rats, and it may weigh up to one pound. It is not a tree climber but lives in or near the ground. The black and Alexandrine rats are good climbers and may nest in shrubs, trees, or in attics. They weigh only about half as much as the brown rat. Because of its habits, the brown rat is often the most destructive of the introduced species, but, as it does not climb much, it is also the rat most easily attacked by the mongoose.

By keeping down the numbers of rats, the mongoose may well have reduced to some extent the amount of bubonic plague, the 'Black Death' of medieval times, on the islands. Plague is caused by *Pasteruella pestis* chiefly transmitted from rat to rat and rat to man by fleas, especially *Xenopsylla cheopis* (Rothschild). Plague first appeared in Hilo on the island of Hawaii in 1900. For the next quarter of a century except for 1901, 1902, and 1916 a few people died of it every year.*

Many kinds of Hawaiian birds are regularly caught and eaten by the mongoose whose taste in birds appears to be indiscriminate. At Pearl Harbor the commonest identifiable remains in mongoose stomachs were those of the peaceful dove, *Geophila tranquilla* (La Rivers, 1948). In their study of 86 scats, Baldwin *et al.* (1952) found that bird remains amounted to only 4 per cent of the food, undoubtedly because of the difficulty of catching birds. It may well be that the damage that the mongoose causes to most kinds

* Plague was unknown in Europe until the introduction of the black rat (or another subspecies of *Rattus rattus*) by the returning navies of the Crusaders in 1095, 1147, and 1191. Curiously enough, this rat had existed in Europe before classical times, as is testified by its remains in the Pliestocene of Lombardy and other places (Barrett-Hamilton & Hinton, 1916). The brown rat, a native of temperate Asia, was first introduced into Europe in 1716 at Copenhagen by the visiting Russian fleet. Within the last two centuries it has almost completely eliminated the black rat from the temperate countries of Europe and much of North America.

of birds is more than compensated for by its destruction of rats.

The mongoose may benefit some birds. For instance, it regularly eats small amounts of fruits, and no less than 29 per cent of the 86 scats mentioned above contained seeds of one kind or another. Some of the seeds pass out undamaged. In this way the mongoose helps to spread fruits such as guava and balsam apple. In spreading the latter, the mongoose has provided food for such game birds as the lace-necked dove (Schwartz & Schwartz, 1951).

Some birds such as adult herons can ward off attacks by the mongoose (La Rivers, 1948). The Hawaiian goose can protect its nest and young when attacked by a single mongoose, but sometimes two or more combine in attacking it and are then able to distract the attention of the adult sufficiently to make off with the young (Baldwin *et al.*, 1952).

It has been claimed that the mongoose prevents the survival of ground-nesting birds in Hawaii. Of course it eats many ground-nesting birds. Nevertheless, it is probable that it is not normally a limiting factor in their survival. Smith & Woodworth (1951) found that the mongoose and possibly feral cats were responsible for the destruction of 36 per cent of the pheasant nests they examined in Hawaii and Maui. More nests were destroyed in areas of sparse vegetation at low altitudes than in dense cover at high altitudes where the mongoose was more abundant. Within the range of the mongoose, the populations of several ground-nesting birds such as the ring-necked pheasant, the Japanese quail, and the skylark are actually equal to or even greater than on those islands without the mongoose. An exception is the California quail which is slightly more common on mongoose-free Niihau than on any island with the mongoose (Fischer, 1951). It is probably quite rightly claimed (Schwartz & Schwartz, 1949, 1950) that climatic conditions and the quality of food, cover, and water are much more important in the survival of non-colonial forms of ground-nesting birds than is predation by the mongoose. The type of habitat suited to the requirements of ground-nesting birds is usually less suitable for mongooses and *vice versa*.

The mongoose may, however, virtually exterminate colonial ground-nesting birds. This has been the fate of the Hawaiian dark-rumped petrel (*Pterodroma phaeopygia*) on several islands. The mongoose may invade a nesting colony and raise its young in burrows made by the birds (Bryan, 1908). The Newell shearwater (*Puffinus newelli*) used to nest in ground burrows on Maui, but in recent years it has only been reported from mongoose-free Kauai (Pearsall, 1947), where several breeding colonies of the wedge-tailed shearwater (*Puffinus pacificus cuneatus*) were reported in 1946 and 1947.

The larger sea birds can rear their young even if the mongoose is present. In January 1947 red-footed boobies (*Sula sula rubripes*) attempted to establish a breeding ground on Mokapu Point, Ohau, but were unsuccessful because they were used for target practice by the military. When this destruction was stopped, 450 pairs began to breed successfully in the area. Many of their nests were built on the ground but most were two to ten feet up in koa haole shrubs. Although mongooses were present, such of their scats as were examined showed only remains of rodents and insects.

It was perhaps to be expected that the mongoose would prove to be innocent of many of the accusations that were levelled against it. Much of the odium in which it is held is undoubtedly due to its predilection for raiding poultry pens and taking both birds and eggs. As we have noted elsewhere, even tame mongooses cannot be broken of this habit. The fact remains that the various game birds introduced into the islands inhabited by it have survived. The Hawaiian goose survived the presence of the mongoose as did a number of sea birds, and some sea birds continue to breed on mongoose infested islands. The ground-nesting Hawaiian owl and skylark are still present on all the major islands.

XII
Indian folk tales

THE abundance of mongooses, their frequent domestication, and particularly their prowess in dealing with deadly snakes inevitably resulted in their becoming important characters in numerous folk tales and legends throughout the Oriental Region. In this chapter we have done no more than select a few tales that illustrate the diversity of the roles given to the mongoose. The only one of these that is well-known outside the Oriental Region is a much modified version of the central tale of Book V of the *Panchatantra*, which we reproduce on another page.

In the *Mahabharat*, one of India's most famous epics, there is the story of the golden mongoose: 'Once the great and pious King Yudhisthir performed a Yangna (holy rite) and gave a feast to the holy men attending it. After the feast a mongoose came and began to roll over the remains of the feast. It was a strange creature. One half of its body was made of gold. Being asked by the people there about his strange appearance and behaviour, the mongoose told the following story. "Long ago there lived a very poor brahman. He was so poor that once he was unable to procure food for his family for seven days. After seven days he got a handful of rice and boiled it to eat. Just at the moment the family was about to take the meal, a stranger appeared at the door and begged for food. A guest at one's door! So without a moment's hesitation the brahman gave all of the food to the stranger. As a consequence of this, the entire family died of starvation. I was living nearby and accidentally touched the remains of the food. This turned half my body into gold. Since then I have been searching all over the world for another man as pious as that brahman, so that by touching the remains of the food offered by him, the other half of my body may be turned into gold. Hearing that the King Yudhisthir is a very pious man, I came here, but it seems that my search is not yet over!" ' This tale is supposed to date from about 1000 B.C.

The five books or five chapters of the *Panchatantra* are stories related by a learned Brahman, Viṣṇuśarman (or Bishnu Sharma).* The better known of the two mongoose stories in the *Panchatantra* occupies all of Book V. It is 'Hasty action, or the brahman and the mongoose'. The translation we have had from Dr G. Ganguly is as follows:

'There was a brahman family. One day a son was born to them and on that very day a female mongoose living in that house gave birth to a young one. But the mother mongoose died the same day. The brahman lady reared the young mongoose along with her own son, feeding them both with her own milk. In spite of her great affection for the young mongoose, there was always the fear in her mind that the mongoose, being a beast, might hurt her little child some day. One day she left her little son sleeping and went out to fetch water. Before going out she asked her husband to keep watch and to protect her child from the mongoose. But the brahman had to go out begging, and so he left the child alone. In the meantime a cobra came out of a hole in the room. The mongoose, though not trained and brought up as an animal, by natural instinct attacked the cobra. He fought with the cobra to save his human brother and cut the cobra into pieces. After saving his brother in this way, in joy he went outside with blood on his mouth to meet the mother. But the mother, on her return saw the blood on his mouth and thought that the mongoose must have killed her son. She threw the pitcher full of water at the mongoose and killed him. She entered the room crying that her baby had been killed by the mongoose, but she found that her son was still sleeping and a cobra, cut into pieces, was lying beside the baby. Then she realised her mistake and repented, crying that she had killed her son the mongoose.'

Edgerton's (1965) translation of the *Panchatantra* is from a Sanskrit version that more nearly approximates the lost original. The story is, however, similar in essentials, but it was the brahman and not his wife who killed the mongoose. His wife had gone to a nearby river to purify herself and wash her soiled garments ten days after the birth of her son. While she was at the river, the brahman received a summons from the queen and left the child.

* The date of the original Sanskrit text, is not yet known. It was in existence about A.D. 500, and it may have been as early as 100 B.C. By 1914 there were over 200 versions in more than 50 languages, and, according to some writers, until the twentieth century its circulation was second only to that of the Bible.

He returned before his wife and met the mongoose, which had its muzzle smeared with blood. Believing that the mongoose had eaten his boy, he slew him with his stick only to discover when he entered the house that the child was lying alseep unhurt.

Emeneau (1940) records a version from the Kotas of South India in which the wife and not the husband kills the mongoose. The Kotas believed they were talking about an event that had taken place about eighteen years previously. Emeneau leaves undecided the question of whether or not the Kota story originated independently of the *Panchatantra*. However, in view of the wide circulation since ancient times of various versions of the story, it is reasonable to suppose that the Kotas were in fact simply repeating the ancient story and were mistaken in thinking that the events had taken place in the twentieth century.

The story of the brahman and the mongoose bears a striking resemblance to the theme of the poem *Llewellyn and his dog* by W. R. Spencer. While Llewellyn was out hunting, his dog Gelert killed a wolf that was attacking his child at home. When Llewellyn returned, Gelert ran out to meet him with bloody paws and mouth. Llewellyn, making the same mistake as the brahman, killed his dog only to repent bitterly when he discovered that his child was safe and the wolf was dead beside him.

Edgerton shows that the story of Llewellyn and his dog is but a modified version of the story of the brahman and the mongoose. He points out that in an Arabic translation of the *Panchatantra* the weasel is substituted for the mongoose.* In the Hebrew version attributed to Joel, the weasel is changed to a dog. We now have a priest or ascetic, a dog, and a snake. In this latter form the story occurs in the collection of Arabic stories known as *Sindibad* or the Seven Sagas, but the cleric has now become an officer or a knight. This collection of stories began to circulate in Europe as early as the twelfth century. It then became generally known as the *Seven Sages of Rome*. The Welsh version dates from the fourteenth century, and the snake was still the animal that was killed.

In a popular form of the story told in Wales in later medieval

* Edgerton (1965, p. 18) says that the substitution was made because the mongoose was '. . . an animal unknown to the Arabs.' Several species of mongooses occur in Arabia. Cheesman (1920) records the fact that Arab children tame them and sell them for a few annas. Furthermore, the small Indian mongoose, *Herpestes auropunctatus*, has several local Arab names (see p. 116).

times, the snake became a wolf, no doubt because it seemed a more natural animal for the dog to attack and also because the only poisonous snake in the country, the viper, is less than 32 inches long and is not particularly dangerous. A Prince Llewellyn did in fact exist, and he had a dog called Gelert. However, Gelert died from exhaustion after an unusually long chase. The association of Llewellyn and his dog with the story of the hasty murder of a faithful dog by his master arose in 1793 or 1794 because of a mistake on the part of a Welsh innkeeper when Spencer visited him six or seven years before he published his poem in 1880.

The fourteenth story of Book 1 of the *Panchatantra* is called, 'Herons, snake, and mongoose'. The translation we have had made is as follows:

'There was a big banyan tree in a certain forest. There lived a black cobra (Krishna Sarpa) in the hollow trunk of the tree. On the tree also lived some herons. The snake used to eat the young herons. One day a certain heron, whose young ones had been eaten up by the snake, was in despair and went to the bank of a pond and sat down in a sorrowful mood. Seeing him in a sorrowful mood, a crab (Kulirak) asked him, "Sir, what can I do?" The heron replied, "Today the cobra has eaten up my children and so out of sorrow I am crying. If you could help me to destroy the snake, I will be very much obliged." The crab thought that snakes and herons were the natural enemies of his class and so decided to take this opportunity to destroy both. The crab advised the heron to scatter small pieces of fish meat from the hole of the mongoose to the hollow of the tree where the snake lived. The mongoose would then follow the trail and reach the hole of the snake and kill it. The heron did as he was advised. Soon the mongoose reached the tree and killed the snake. But he also climbed the banyan tree and killed the whole family of herons. Moral: do not believe an enemy posing as a friend.'

This translation agrees fairly well with the version published by Edgerton (1965) except that in the latter the kind of snake is not specified.

In the Bengali literature there are a number of stories about the snake goddess Manasa. Some of these mention the mongoose. In the religious ceremonies that take place during the rainy season in Bengal, Bihar, Orissa, and other places, stories such as the following are read: 'A merchant, Chand Sadagar from Champanagar, was cursed by the goddess Manasa who told him that he would die of snake bite on his wedding night. To save himself he had the walls of the room he was to occupy on his wedding night built of iron. As a further protection against snakes, he kept mongooses and peacocks in it. But when the walls were being made, Manasa threatened the builder and asked him to leave a crack which could not be detected by other people in one of the walls. So the builder of the room left a fine crack in one of the walls. Through that crack a female black snake entered the room where Chand Sadagar and his wife Behula were sleeping on their wedding night. The snake lay near the bed of Chand Sadagar because unless he hurt her she would not bite him. In his sleep Chand Sadagar by chance stretched his leg so that he hurt the snake, which bit him and left the room through the crack in the wall. He cried out and Behula woke. She

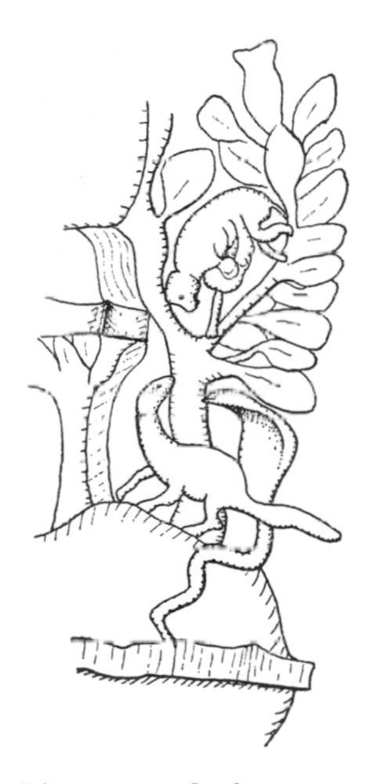

Fig. 14. From a stone carving near the dagaba of Thurparama in the ancient city of Anuradhpura, Ceylon. The dagaba was erected in the reign of King Dewanampia Tissa (307-267 B.C.). A mongoose attacks a cobra while a monkey holding its baby looks down. (After Mitton)

took him out and after a great deal of sacrifice saved his life.' The manuscript of this story can be traced back as far as A.D. 1400, but it was first printed by V. Gupta in A.D. 1600.

The mongoose is mentioned in early Indian medical books such as *Charak Sanhita* (*ca.* A.D. 100) and *Susrata*, in which it is called *sarpa baidya* or snake doctor. An old belief is that after a snake bite the mongoose will go and fetch an antidote, usually a herb of some kind (see p. 17).

It may be noted here that in Ceylon in the ancient city of

Anuradhpura, near the dagaba of Thurparama erected in the reign of King Dewanampia Tissa (307-267 B.C.), is a stone carving showing the mongoose attacking a cobra. Fig. 14 is from a drawing of this carving published by Mitton (1916). The date of the carving is not known, at least not to us, and it may have been made long after the dagaba was erected. Fights between the cobra and the mongoose do not appear to have been staged in Ceylon until comparatively recent times because of the semi-sacred nature of the reptile. However, by the sixteenth century such fights were commonly staged by the Portuguese (Orta, 1563).

XIII
In Ancient Egypt

REPRESENTATIONS of the mongoose (*Herpestes ichneumon*) can be found on the walls of tombs and temples of Thebes and Saqqara. The earliest date from the Old Kingdom (2800-2150 B.C.) and usually show the mongoose marauding. The two reproduced (Fig. 15) occur in fishing and fowling scenes in which the principal figures are human hunters, but there is nothing in the rest of the scene to indicate that the mongoose is not hunting entirely on its own account.

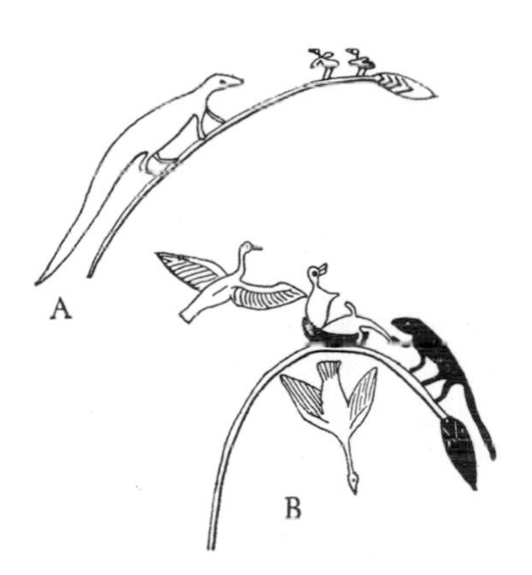

Fig. 15. Decorations at Thebes. (A) Sculpture of a mongoose attacking birds. (B) A mongoose carrying away a young bird from the nest. (After Wilkinson)

All animals seem to have been of interest to the Egyptians; very many of them were venerated as sacred. In worshipping a great variety of cult objects, animals among them, the prehistoric Egyptian was in no way different from other inhabitants of Africa or other parts of the world at the same stage of development. Elsewhere the sacred animal tended to have religious significance for a quality it possessed in relation to man: it might, like the lion, inspire fear through its strength and hunting skill, or, like the goat, gratitude because of some service it performed. To the Egyptians the animal was significant in its own right. In a universe seen to be unchanging in its total aspect but constantly disintegrating and renewing itself in detail, animals usually more notable to man for general characteristics than for individual features seemed more at home in their surroundings than the human onlooker felt himself to be in his. Itwas appropriate that these creatures should be associated with the gods of the universe.

The relationship between the god and the animal varied. The animal might be the servant of the incarnation of the god but the animal itself was not the god and the incarnation did not limit the god's powers. Representations of the gods illustrated developing theories as to their nature . In protohistoric times the spirit of the god dwelt in a particular animal and could be represented by an image of the animal. About the beginning of the 1st Dynasty (3200 B.C.) the animal image is given human arms, an indication that the god's powers were greater than those of the natural animal. By the end of the 2nd Dynasty (2800 B.C.) the image combines animal and human characteristics, and from the 3rd Dynasty onwards there is a tendency for the animal features to be replaced by human ones. Until comparatively late times, however, many gods continued to be shown with animal or bird heads and all retained their association with their own special animals.

The long history of Egypt includes periods of weakness and foreign domination and also of national self confidence and success. One such latter period began in 663 B.C. when Ethiopian control of the country came to an end and Psammetichus I set up an independent and unified Kingdom. Actuated by a zeal for reform and longing for the glories of the past, the court and priesthood set about a systematic revival of the social and religious practices of the Old Kingdom, a period which had come to an end a thousand years before. Such archaising movements are rarely successful and even more rarely are the institutions of the past precisely reproduced. In this case the attempt succeeded in producing a renaissance of native art and religion. The ancient religious forms were, however, in some respects misunderstood and particularly was this so of the relationship between god and animal. The result was that the subsequent centuries were marked by so extensive a cult of sacred animals as to excite the wonder and occasional derision of the rest of the civilised world. One of the many animals venerated was the mongoose.

The Egyptian pantheon contained an exceptionally large number of different gods. Many of them belonged to a particular locality and the importance of their cult depended on the political importance at different times of the district of their origin. During the very long period—three and a half thousand years—from which there remain records of religious observances, there were many such fluctuations in the power and prestige of individual gods and several identifications of the principal gods. This, together with a readiness to accept any new local god and attach him to a god already recognised, produces a theological system of great complexity. It is not surprising that the mongoose was associated with the several gods in different places and embodied more than one characteristic. Archaeological finds and inscriptions link it with the gods Atum, Re, and Horus. It was sacred to Mafdet, who was the goddess who protected against snake bites. Aelian says it was connected with the worship of Buto, whom he identified with the Roman Latona, and Bubastis in whom he recognised Lucina.

The most interesting religious ideas connected with the mongoose are found in the worship of Horus of Letopolis, the god of light and darkness, of sight and blindness, in whom day and night were one. It may be, as Brunner-Traut (1965) suggests, that the Egyptians failed to distinguish between the shrew mouse (Soricidae) and the mongoose and thought that the former was the nocturnal manifestation of the latter. The difference in the size of the two animals—the shrew mouse (species of *Crocidura*) measures only about seven inches from the nose to the tip of the tail—could be explained by the theory that as night fell the mongoose shrank in size, regaining its former appearance when the sun rose the following morning. As the shrew mouse is usually only seen at night and the mongoose during the day, the hypothesis could survive for a long time, and the difference in the habits of the two animals would be accepted merely as another feature of the metamorphosis. Certainly as late as the ninth century A.D. it was believed that the mongoose could alter its size at will. Al-Gahiz, the Arabian natural historian who died in 868, says, 'In Egypt there is an animal called Nims. It is able to contract and to become smaller until it is like a mouse. If then a snake winds round it, it takes a deep breath, puffs itself up and so breaks the snake in pieces.' A similar belief was recorded by his contemporary Ibn Qutaiba.

Again in the worship of Atum of Heliopolis the mongoose was credited with the ability to alter its size, this time to an enormous length so that even the sun god who sees all, could not see both head and tail at the same time. Here the animal's characteristics were thought to be similar to those implied by the Greek name ichneumon, the 'tracker' or 'pursuer', for the mongoose saw, heard, and smelt out all that happened in the world. The god of Letopolis also fought the dangerous thunder-snake Apophis during storms: this too is a reflection of the natural role of the mongoose.

The greatest number of representations of the mongoose made by the ancient Egyptians date, as might be expected, from the Graeco-Roman period (after 332 B.C.) when the cult of sacred animals was at its height. These include small bronzes of well-defined types

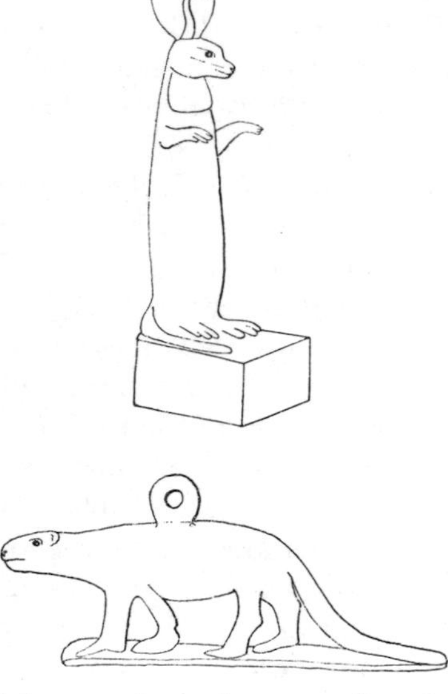

Fig. 16. (TOP) Bronze of mongoose with sun disc and uraeus. (BOTTOM) Amulet in the form of a mongoose. (After Roeder)

which must have been produced in great numbers. Some of these are of the mongoose walking, with the legs in such a position that all four can be seen from the side. Others show the animal in the low-sit position and the head may carry the sun disc and the uraeus or sacred asp (Fig. 16 Top). Some were used as amulets (Fig. 16 Bottom) and others as votive offerings.

Occasionally mongooses were embalmed when they died. Mummies of mongooses have been found inside small bronze statues of the lion-headed goddess Uto. Sometimes the mummies were packed into small coffins, the lids of which were decorated with either paintings or models of the living animal.

XIV
Mongooses as pets

THE mongooses that are most readily tamed and become the most satisfactory pets are, as might be expected, those that are gregarious and diurnal such as the meerkat, the banded mongoose, and the dwarf mongoose. Their need for social contact is so great that they quickly come to accept a human as a substitute companion. Some of the diurnal species that hunt in pairs or in small family parties, such as the Indian mongoose, make good pets if caught when they are young (Plate III, facing p. 14). However, most species of mongooses are solitary or hunt in pairs and make poor pets as a consequence. But even *Ichneumia*, which is nocturnal and hunts alone or in pairs, is said to make a pleasing pet if caught young enough. Skulls found in houses at Merkes, Babylon (Koldeway, 1914) suggests that even in these early times (*ca.* 600 B.C.) mongooses were household pets.

Mongooses often become very attached to the people they know and will attack strangers (e.g. Dücker, 1965; Ewer, 1963a). Powell (1913) says of *Herpestes auropunctatus*, 'As for the servants and strangers, she will not allow them anywhere near her young, but allows us to handle them.' Some species, such as meerkats, like to creep into their owner's clothing, when it may be supposed that social contact as well as physical contact with the burrow wall is probably important.

Mongooses will learn to recognise their pet names and will come if a reward is likely to follow. They quickly learn to respond to a noise or a call that never signifies anything but food. For instance, an Indian mongoose would always immediately run to the noise of bran being shaken in a dish from which it was always fed some mealworms. Even such social species as meerkats never appear to be motivated by any desire to please their owners: unlike dogs, but like cats, they appear to do only those things that please them.

Many writers have described the behaviour as pets of mongooses they or others have kept as pets. Walker (1942) has given an account of how to care for captive mongooses, and Daglish (1958) also has a few notes on their care. For the convenience of the reader who may wish to read about the species he is keeping as a pet, a number of these accounts are cited under the headings of the species. The more detailed accounts are indicated by an asterisk.

Herpestes auropunctatus: Cheesman (1920), Prater (1935), Powell (1913*).

Herpestes edwardsi: Adie (1829*), Anon. (1936), Blanford (1888), Daglish (1958), Fischer (1921), Frere (1929), Jerdon (1867), Lloyd-Jones (1953), Phillips (1935), Rensch and Dücker (1959*), Webb-Peploe (1947).

Herpestes ichneumon: Anderson (1902), Dücker (1960*), Heller (1937*), Rensch and Dücker (1959*), Shortridge (1934), Wilkinson (1879).

Herpestes smithi: Hill (1956), Phillips (1954).

Herpestes urva: Brownlow (1940b).

Atilax: Cansdale (1946), Haagner (1920), Stevenson-Hamilton (1947).

Helogale parvula: Pitman (1954), Shortridge (1934), Stevenson-Hamilton (1947), Taylor & Webb (1955*).

Mungos mungo: Ansell (1960), Kinloch (1964*), Loveridge (1944*), Shortridge (1934), Stevenson-Hamilton (1947), Vossler (1907).

Crossarchus obscurus: Cansdale (1946), Durrell (1958*), Naundorff (1936*).

Suricata: Daglish (1958), Dücker (1962*), Ewer (1963a*), Hall (1926), Heck (1956), Martin (1891), Stevenson-Hamilton (1947).

XV
Portraits of some species

MUCH more is known about the habits of *Herpestes auropunctatus* and *H. edwardsi* than about any other mongooses. It was therefore inevitable that a book about the natural history of mongooses should be largely one about these two species and to a lesser extent the meerkat. As one consequence of this, no coherent account appears of the natural history of any of the other species. This chapter is made necessary to remedy this defect: it contains brief outlines of the natural history of seven species, which are the only ones about which enough is known to write more than a few sentences. For instance, practically nothing is known about the natural history of *Liberiictis*, *Rhynchogale*, *Bdeogale*, or *Paracynictis*.

Atilax is probably the largest of all mongooses and *Helogale parvula* the smallest. In all species the largest males are appreciably longer and heavier than the largest females. The length in inches and the weight in pounds of large males of a number of species is as follows:

	Head and body	*Tail*	*Weight*
Herpestes auropunctatus	15	12	2·8
Herpestes edwardsi	19·5	16·5	6
Herpestes fuscus	19·5	13	6
Herpestes smithi	18	18	6
Herpestes ichneumon	24	21·5	
Herpestes sanguineus	13·5	12	
Herpestes vitticollis	21	13	7·5
Herpestes urva	23	16·5	6
Atilax paludinosus	24	21·5	
Helogale parvula	9	8	1·5
Mungos mungo	18	12	
Crossarchus obscurus	16·5	10	2·9
Ichneumia albicauda	24	19	9·9
Rhynchogale melleri	19	16	
Bdeogale crassicauda	18	12	
Paracynictis selousi	19	16	
Cynictis penicillata	15	11	
Suricata suricatta	14	10	

A short sketch of the biology of the kusimanse has been given by Walker (1964). However, despite his awareness of the confusion in the literature between *Crossarchus obscurus* and the banded mongoose, it seems clear that he has fallen into the same trap: his remarks about the hunting of the kusimanse, their method of breaking hard objects, and the statement that they prefer the open veldt are clearly taken from papers about the banded mongoose under the name of *Crossarchus fasciatus*. A good account of the method used by the kusimanse in the Cameroons when hunting for crabs and frogs in shallow water is given by Durrell (1958).

THE SLENDER MONGOOSE

Herpestes (*Galerella*) *sanguineus* (Fig. 17) is found in a wide variety of habitats in most of Africa: low, forest, lightly wooded country,

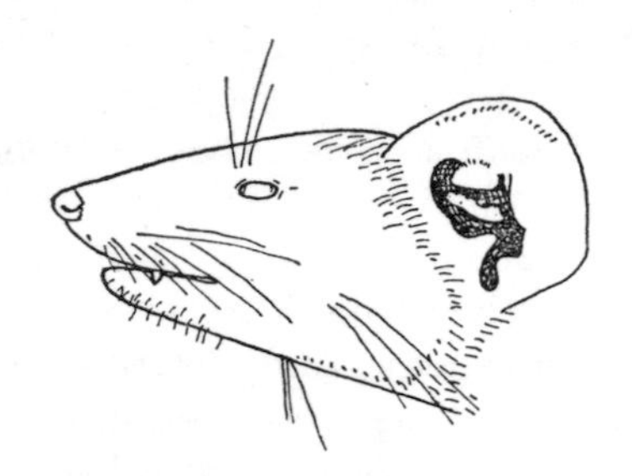

Fig. 17. Head of *Herpestes sanguineus* with ear open. (After Pocock)

thick scrub, and open or lightly covered plains. It is chiefly diurnal but will continue to hunt until well after dusk, and it occasionally wanders about on moonlight nights, especially during the warmer months. It hunts singly or in pairs. In wooded country it is fond of sleeping and breeding in hollow trees, but in more open country in crevices amongst rocks or in burrows. It often lies up during the heat of the day. It is an expert tree climber and will catch birds amongst the branches. When pursued it may flash up a tree trunk and disappear in the manner of a squirrel. The slender mongoose feeds on small rodents, birds, lizards, snakes, insects, and fruits and berries. It will kill and eat the deadly mamba. Poultry yards are sometimes raided and the eggs and chickens eaten. It will eat carrion and will come to traps baited with any kind of meat (Stevenson-Hamilton, 1947). It sometimes enters gardens and scratches up the ground nuts.

The slender mongoose is the least tamable of the mongooses, and Cansdale (personal communication) has been unable to tame them satisfactorily even when they were hand-reared. Unfortunately, this mongoose is often also known as the dwarf mongoose, especially in West Africa, a name more properly applied to *Helogale parvula.*

A common legend about *H. sanguineus* is that it lies on the ground and exposes its scent glands as bait for fowls. When the fowl swallows one, the gland expands and chokes the fowl. This is one of the versions of the legend common among the Ashanti hunters (e.g. Cansdale, 1946), but there are many other versions, none of which is in any way based upon fact. Occasionally similar stories are told about *Atilax* and other mongooses.

Little is known of the habits of *H.* (*G.*) *pulverulentus* and other species of the subgenus *Galerella*, but they appear to be similar. *G. pulverulentus* is a vector of rabies in South Africa (Snyman, 1940), but it is only of minor importance as compared with *Cynictis* and *Suricata.*

THE WATER MONGOOSE

Atilax paludinosus (Fig. 18), which is the most heavily built of the African mongooses, is nocturnal and seldom seen during the day.

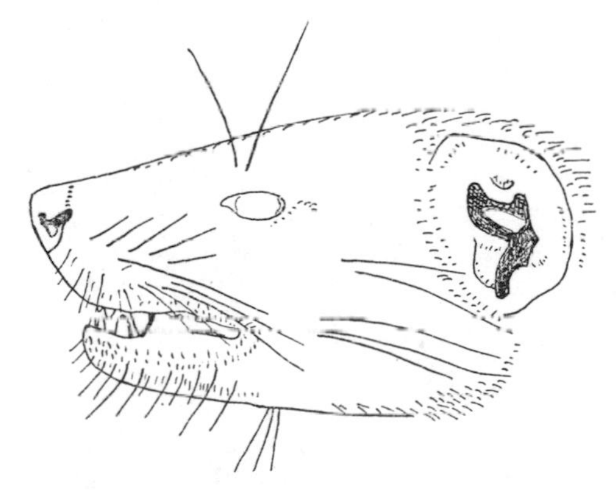

Fig. 18. Head of *Atilax paludinosus* with ear open. (After Pocock)

It lives on the edges of reed-fringed rivers, swamps, and estuaries. Of all the mongooses it is the most aquatic and is rarely found far from permanent open water. It swims and dives well. When swimming part of its back as well as its head is usually exposed. At dusk or on moonlight nights it is sometimes seen making rapidly across a broad stretch of water. When it is pursued it may dive into the river and swim beneath the surface until it reaches a clump of weeds near the opposite bank, where it will sometimes remain for a long time completely submerged with only its nose sticking out above the surface (Sclater, 1900).

Although this mongoose is more at home in the water than any other species, it is the only one that has toes (Fig. 19) entirely without webs (Pocock, 1916). In this respect its feet resemble those of racoons, which have rather similar feeding habits and use their delicate digits to feel for aquatic animals in the mud or beneath the edges of submerged stones.

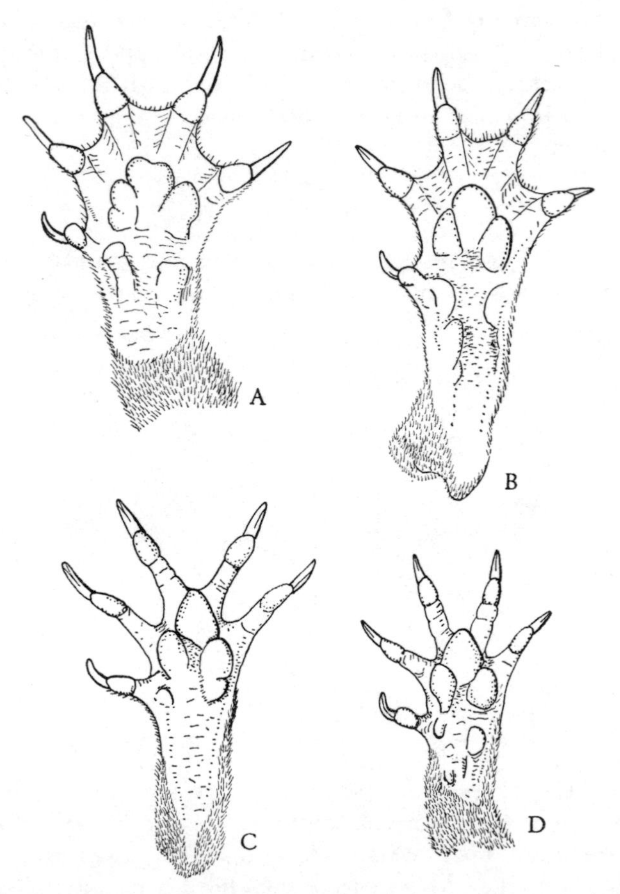

Fig. 19. (A) Left front foot of *Herpestes smithi*. (B) Left hind foot of same. (C) Left front foot of *Atilax paludinosus*. (D) Left hind foot of same. In *Atilax* the interdigital webs have been lost so that the digits are separated right down to the plantar pad. (After Pocock)

The water mongoose preys on fresh-water crabs and frogs and sometimes catches fish. It also eats cane rats (*Otomys*) and other swamp rodents, birds, reptiles, and insects. It will occasionally raid poultry yards. Hard-shelled prey is sometimes broken by flinging it down on to a hard surface (Steinbacher, 1939, 1951; Lombard, 1958). An instance is reported of one that fed on the head of a puff adder and then died. When it was later dissected, it was found that the fangs of the snake had pierced the wall of the stomach. It is said that together with the water monitor lizard it is perhaps the most deadly enemy of the crocodile, scratching out from the sand and eating the eggs whenever it can (Stevenson-Hamilton, 1947).

It breeds in burrows in the banks of rivers and swamps and apparently also sometimes in nests that they make by gathering masses of vegetation into heaps in the reed beds. Floating masses of vegetation and grassy patches on the banks are used as resting and feeding places. It is said to become very tame in captivity.

THE DWARF MONGOOSE

Helogale parvula (Fig. 20) is diurnal and gregarious. It is often seen hunting in groups of four to fifteen, '. . . keeping all the time

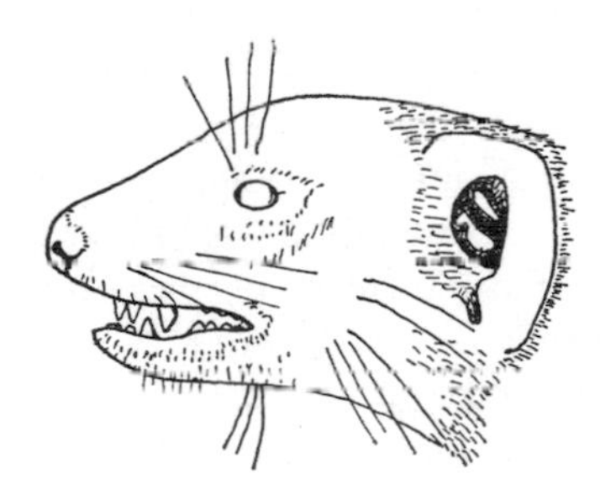

Fig. 20. Head of *Helogale parvula* with ear open. (After Pocock)

in close formation like small packs of beagles.' (Shortridge, 1934.) Many writers (e.g. Heller, 1911) comment upon their incessant chirping to each other as they hunt. They apparently have no fixed abode, although they return periodically to good hunting grounds. At night or when pursued they often take refuge in the funnels of termite mounds, in hollow trees, or in crevices in rocks, but they occasionally dig their own burrows.

Their food probably consists chiefly of insects, but they also eat eggs of birds and reptiles, mice, small birds, lizards, snakes, snails, and earthworms. Several may co-operate in killing a snake. Sometimes they dig out and eat trap-door spiders. Fruits and berries are also eaten.

The young are often born in burrows, sometimes in termite mounds, but the mother will also construct a nest in long grass, which she carefully covers over when she leaves to go hunting (Stevenson-Hamilton, 1947). Two to six young are born (Taylor & Webb, 1955). The dwarf mongoose is said to become exceptionally tame in captivity.

THE BANDED MONGOOSE

Mungos mungo (Plate XI, opposite) is diurnal and goes about in packs usually of about six to twenty which maintain a compact formation when travelling. Sometimes an entire colony takes refuge in a rock shelter or warren with only one or two entrances. In level sandy country, whether open or wooded, they live in ordinary warrens. The burrows, unlike those of the meerkat, are usually concealed under clumps of bush. Sometimes an individual may sit up on its haunches and look about when hunting, but they do not sit up and look around outside their burrows in the manner of the yellow mongoose and the meerkat.

'Whether moving about or at rest banded mongoose are inclined to be noisy, and, even when below ground or under piles of loose rocks, their subdued chattering and grunting sounds at times betray their presence.' (Shortridge, 1934.) On the whole they keep to regular hours, returning to their hiding places at about the same time every evening. Packs out hunting are easily observed because they seem to be rather unsuspicious. They hunt at all hours in cool or cloudy weather, but on sunny days are most frequently seen in the early morning or late afternoon. Hunting is accompanied by a great deal of low chattering, and '. . . several individuals may sometimes crowd together in a friendly manner, like a brood of chicken, to investigate and share in any special food discovery.' (Shortridge, 1934.)

Shortridge describes an unusually large colony of about thirty that inhabited the crevices of an old stone weir. During the day the members of the colony went off in several different troops which hunted independently up and down the rocky sluits in the neighbourhood. In the evening they all came back to play about between the stones of the weir until dark.

In East Africa they are common on the grassy plains where they live in colonies on the open veld. According to Heller (1911),

Plate XI. *Mungos mungo*, the banded mongoose. (S. Dunton, New York Zoological Society)

Plate XII. *Cynictis penicillata*, the yellow mongoose.

'They, however, do not stop long in any locality, but move about in small packs of ten to twenty individuals which take up a temporary abode in any nest of burrows which they find convenient. From our observations it was apparent that they do not remain more than a day or two in any one set of burrows.' Packs of 10 to 100 have been recorded in Somaliland (Drake-Brockman, 1910).

They feed chiefly on insects, centipedes, and snails. They also eat mice, small reptiles, the eggs and young of ground-nesting birds, and fruits and berries. Eggs and snails are broken by dashing them against a stone (see p. 6). The banded mongoose becomes very tame in captivity.

THE WHITE-TAILED MONGOOSE

Ichneumia albicauda (Fig. 21) is nocturnal and prefers localities where there is plenty of thick cover, such as the edges of forests or

Fig. 21. Head of *Ichneumia albicauda* with ear open. (After Pocock)

ravines with an abundance of tangled undergrowth. During the day it lies up in porcupine or aardvark burrows, cavities under the roots of trees, or shelters amongst rocks. In secluded places it comes out in search of food in the afternoons, but it is otherwise strictly nocturnal (Fitzsimons, 1919). The white-tailed mongoose hunts singly or in pairs. It is said to bark like a small dog. It preys upon mice, rats, rock dassies (*Procavia*), and other mammals up to the size of hares and birds up to the size of guinea fowl. It also eats eggs, lizards, snakes, and insects. One individual had a small cobra in its stomach.

It will raid poultry yards. Pitman (1954) says that on moonlight nights the white-tailed mongoose was sometimes seen to dance outside the wire netting of poultry pens. This excited the curiosity of the fowls, which sometimes stuck their heads out through the wire netting to see better and had them bitten off promptly.

Their claws are not adapted for climbing, and, according to Roberts (1951), there appear to be no records of their doing so. However, Roosevelt (1910) claims that they prey on tree hyraxes and follow them everywhere amongst the tree tops. He also says that they are hated by the Ndorobo because they rob honey buckets. It seems fairly certain that Roosevelt is speaking of some other animal.

When it is attacked, it may use its anal glands in defence (Pitman, 1954), a habit also recorded for the Oriental *H. urva* and *H. vitticollis*. In captivity they are the wildest and shyest of the African mongooses, showing themselves only at night (Haagner, 1920). However, they are said to become pleasing pets if captured young enough.

THE YELLOW MONGOOSE

Cynictis penicillata (Plate XII, facing p. 99, Figs. 22, 23) lives in karoo and high grass-veld country. It is diurnal and gregarious. Sometimes only a pair or a family are found in a single burrow with a double outlet, but they more commonly live in warrens with numerous entrances that communicate beneath the surface. Colonies of about 50 individuals have been recorded. They sit on their haunches or stand up on their toes outside their burrows in the same rigid, marmot-like attitudes of the meerkat and the ground squirrel (*Geoscirus inauris* (Zimm)). They have often been recorded living, apparently amicably, in the same series of burrows as the meerkat and ground squirrel (e.g. Roberts, 1923, 1951; Shortridge, 1934), and the young of all three species have been seen playing together (Powell *in* Shortridge, 1934). Although it has been said that they eat the young of the ground squirrel, Shortridge thinks they only rarely do so and then only when the parent ground squirrels are away.

It usually uses burrows dug by other animals, chiefly the ground squirrel. Sometimes these two species inhabit very large warrens that may be up to 50 yards wide and have as many as 100 openings. Snyman found that when the colonies were dug up the bedding in the chambers inhabited by the squirrels had fresh straw, whereas in the chambers inhabited by the mongoose bedding was lacking, or it was old or decayed. A characteristic feature of such warrens is that all of the tunnels are at the same level, and only rarely does one pass beneath another. They are generally two to three feet beneath the surface, according to the nature of the soil.

Although the yellow mongoose seldom digs its own warrens, it will do so in soft or sandy soil. The actual digging and most of the

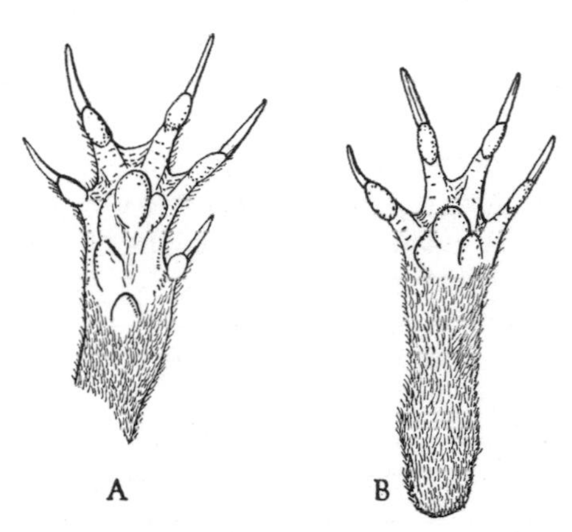

Fig. 22. (A) Right front foot of *Cynictis penicillata.* (B) Right hind foot of same. This is the only species of mongoose with five toes on the front feet and four on the hind feet. All other mongooses have either five or four toes on both front and hind feet. (After Pocock)

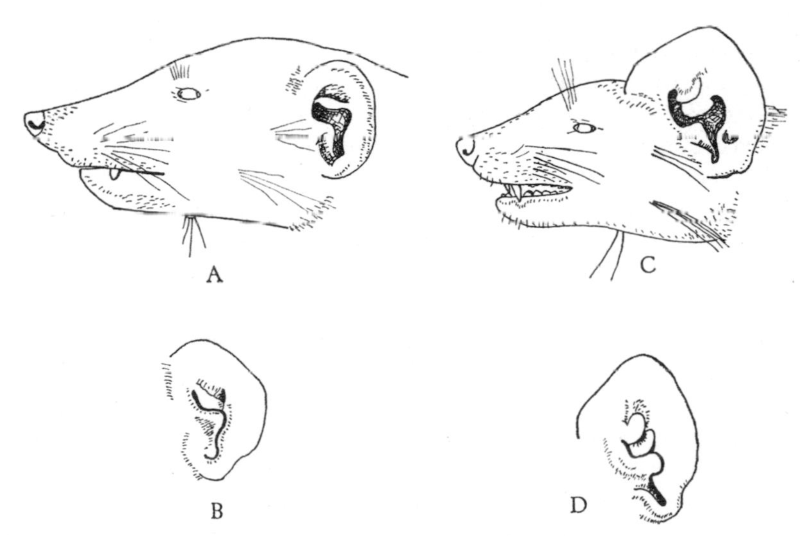

Fig. 23. (A) Head of *Cynictis penicillata* with ear open. (B) Ear of same species closed. (C) Head of *Suricata suricatta* with ear open. (D) Ear of same species closed. (After Pocock)

cleaning up of the burrows occurs after good rains when the soil is moist and easily worked (Snyman, 1940). Where there are 'trassie-bos' mounds that result from wind-blown sand accumulating around *Acacia stolonifera* bushes, nearly every mound is excavated to form a place of refuge. In these mounds, which may be as high as three to five feet and ten to twenty yards wide, the burrows never penetrate below ground level. Sometimes colonies are found on the slopes of very stony hills, but in such places *Cynictis* burrows under large rocks where the soil is soft. It prefers the higher ground or ridges, and, except for very dry seasons, it avoids flat and low-lying plains, presumably to avoid the water-logging that is likely to occur in such places.

When hunting they wander about alone or in pairs far from their burrows, sometimes even a mile or two (Haagner, 1920). They do not dig or scratch about with the characteristic frequency of the meerkat or banded mongoose. Although as a rule the bulk of their food probably consists of locusts, termites, beetles, and other insects, they also eat rats, mice, small birds, eggs of birds and reptiles, tortoises, lizards, and snakes. They seem to be more inclined to attack medium-sized vertebrates than *Mungos*, *Helogale*, or *Suricata*. For instance, they will attack hares and game birds, and in the Eastern Cape Province are recorded killing new-born lambs (Fitzsimons, 1919).

In some areas the harvester termite, *Hodotermes*, is very abundant, and in such areas this insect may be the yellow mongoose's chief food for the greater part of the year. Fourie (1936) showed that its droppings consist almost entirely of fur during the height of an epizootic among gerbilles, but becomes normal again when the incidence of the disease falls. The reason for this is that when the rodents are diseased they fall easy victims to the mongoose. The public health authorities now recognise the fact that when rodent fur is common in the droppings of the yellow mongoose it is evidence that plague or some other epizootic is affecting small rodents.

When living close to villages they may take to hunting at night. *Cynictis* does not become as tame and friendly as the meerkat, and it appears to be seldom kept as a pet. They probably breed more than once during a season because females in full lactation have been found to be pregnant. A litter of two is usual, but up to four are recorded.

Cynictis has attracted most attention as a vector of rabies. In many parts of South Africa the incidence of rabies corresponds very closely with its distribution, and the incidence of the disease varies as the population density of the yellow mongoose. By 1940 the yellow mongoose had been responsible for at least 21 human deaths, besides causing some 80 known outbreaks of rabies. A very large proportion of the human deaths were children who attempted to catch what appeared to be a tame mongoose but was in fact a rabid one (Snyman, 1940). It is the most important vector of the disease in South Africa. This is not because it is more susceptible than other animals to the virus, but because it lives in small colonies that are close to each other so that the virus is readily transmitted from one colony to another.

THE MEERKAT

Suricata suricatta is confined to South Africa where it is one of the most characteristic inhabitants of the karro and high grass-veld. It is found principally in the dry western part although it extends to the eastern escarpment, but only in the plains. It is relatively independent of water, and no type of veld seems to be too arid for it. It is never found in forest country.

Meerkats are diurnal, emerging shortly after sunrise and retiring at dusk. In rocky areas they may live in crevices amongst the rocks, but they generally live in burrows. An average colony consists of two dozen or more individuals. They frequently live with the ground squirrel, *Geoscirus inauris* (Zimm.) and occasionally both with the latter and the yellow mongoose (*Cynictis*), the burrows of all three species being similar in appearance. They are energetic diggers and may be equally responsible with the squirrels for the original excavations (Shortridge, 1934), or they may leave most of the work of excavation to the squirrels (Ewer, 1963a). In any event, the squirrels give ground to the meerkats without a fight, and the latter behave as if the squirrels were invisible to them. The burrows of the meerkats (Fig. 24) are close together, numerous entrances amongst the mounds formed by excavated earth leading to passages three to six inches wide deep underground (Roberts, 1923). In areas where they are persecuted, they frequently wander off and live in pairs, seeking less exposed situations for their burrows (Fitzsimons, 1919).

The meerkat (Plate XIV, facing p. 105) is less active than the yellow mongoose, and it does not as a rule wander very far from the burrows, around which it spends most of its time '. . . busily and restlessly scratching in the sand for insects. . . . Whilst digging and hunting about it makes an incessant low grunting sound, quite unlike the bird-like chirping of *Helogale* and *Mungos*.' (Shortridge, 1934.)

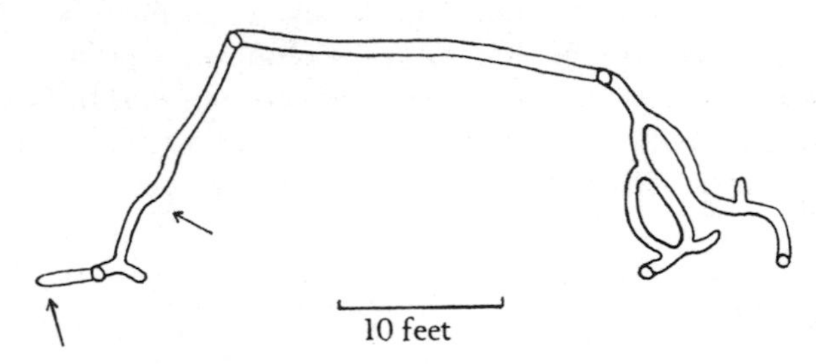

Fig. 24. A simple meerkat warren. The arrows indicate the points where two ground squirrels were found after the meerkats had been gassed. (After Snyman)

Unlike the yellow mongoose, meerkat colonies frequently migrate. This is probably necessary because they do not hunt far from their warrens and therefore soon exhaust local food supplies. Sometimes a colony will occupy at different times during the season warrens that may be a mile or more apart. They apparently breed throughout the year, and litters of as many as five young have been found in one nest.

They feed mainly on insects, spiders, and centipedes and also on eggs of birds and reptiles, rats, mice, small birds, lizards, snakes, snails, and tubers of certain plants. Unlike the yellow mongoose, they do not seem to be in the habit of preying on medium-sized vertebrates, nor do there appear to be records of them raiding poultry yards. A tame individual was once discovered in a hen's nest surrounded by and on friendly terms with the newly-hatched chickens (Shortridge, 1934). Avocado pear seems to be a favourite food, and wild meerkats will come into a farm garden to eat fallen avocados.

'No other wild animal adapts itself to domestic surroundings and conditions more readily . . . and it is a common sight to see tame individuals running about in South African farms.' (Shortridge, 1934.) Their need for social contact is so great that in the absence of their fellows a human is readily accepted as a substitute companion. They become very attached to people they know, but are liable to attack strangers. In captivity they eat meat, poultry, eggs, cheese, and milk, and they readily accept a wide variety of fruits and vegetables such as green peas, carrot, tomato, and banana.

Plate XIII. A pet Indian mongoose.

Plate XIV. A young meerkat.

XVI
Diseases and parasites

LIKE almost all other wild animals, mongooses suffer from very many diseases and parasites, and today probably only a small proportion of these are known. Wild animals that become diseased tend to hide, and they probably rarely recover from serious ailments: unless very large numbers die over a short period of time they escape attention.

Papers reporting the deaths of captive mongooses due to or accelerated by carcinomas of various kinds, myeloid leukemia, cystic thyroids, chronic interstitial nephritis, haemorrhagic hepatitis, cirrhosis of the liver, chronic bronchitis, rickets, and senile arteriosclerosis are cited in Halloran (1955).

No attempt has been made to catalogue all of the diseases and parasites that have been recorded in wild or captive mongooses, but some indication is given of the range of diseases and parasites to which they are prone. The most extensive list of references to papers on the diseases and parasites of mongooses is that of Halloran (1955), and this work should be consulted if further information is sought under any of the following headings:

Viruses. The mongoose as a vector of rabies has already been discussed (p. 73) with special reference to the West Indies. Various species of mongooses, especially the meerkat and the yellow mongoose, have attracted attention as vectors of canine rabies in South Africa. (e.g. Cluver, 1927; de Koch, 1938; Neitz, 1937; Thomas & Neitz, 1933). A virus causing acute pneumonitis in human patients has been recovered from a mongoose (Weir & Horsfall, 1940).

Rickettsia. Rickettsias are very small and strictly intracellular parasites believed to be related to bacteria. Such human diseases as louse-borne epidemic typhus and trench fever are caused by kinds of rickettsias. Heisch *et al.* (1962) found that in Kenya *Herpestes sanguineus*, *Bdeogale crassicauda*, and *Ichneumia* had antibodies for various rickettsias, including *Dermacentroxenus akari*, which causes a tick-borne disease known as rickettsialpox. *Herpestes* and *Bdeogale* had antibodies for *D. conorii*, another tick-borne disease known as boutonneuse fever around the Mediterranean and as tick typhus or tick-bite fever in Africa and Asia. The common reservoirs of these human diseases are usually dogs and rodents. The discovery of antibodies in mongooses means that they too can be suspected of serving as reservoir hosts.

Bacteria. The Indian mongoose dying in captivity has been found to be infected with tuberculosis (Hamerton, 1934, 1935).

Protozoa. A kind of leptospirosis of man known as Weil's disease or infectious jaundice is caused by the spirochete, *Leptospira icterohaemorrhagiae.* It is prevalent in mongooses in Puerto Rico (Alexander *et al.*, 1963). Leptospirosis is also found in the mongoose in Hawaii (Alicata, 1944; Alicata & Breaks, 1943; Minette, 1961, 1964; Yeager *in* Pimental, 1955a). It is found in the kidney tubules of the mongoose. The mongoose is probably infected by eating the brown rat, which seems to be the chief carrier of the disease. Some people in the Hawaiian islands eat mongooses, and it has been suggested that one of the dangers of this habit is the possibility of contracting leptospirosis and also the dangerous nematode, *Trichinella spiralis.*

Accounts have been given of protozoa in the meerkat (Fantham, 1923) and other mongooses (Dubey & Pande, 1963; Hamerton, 1941; Knowles & Gupta, 1931; Neitz, 1938). Perhaps the most interesting of these is the *Entamoeba coli* reported by Hamerton. This is the most common of the harmless amoebas in the human intestine, and it is present in about half the human population.

Worms. Three groups of 'worms' infect mongooses: trematodes or flukes, cestodes or tapeworms, and nematodes. The list given below includes most of the species that have been recorded from mongooses.

Herpestes auropunctatus

Nematoda.	*Trichinella spiralis*
Cestoda.	*Mathevotaenia amphisbeteta* Meggitt (1924a)
	Mathevotaenia hardoiensis Johri (1961)
	Sparganum sp. (Meggitt, 1924a)

Herpestes brachyurus

Trematoda.	*Concinum dathei* Odening (1960)

Plate XV. The banded mongoose.

Plate XVI. A pet Indian mongoose.

Herpestes edwardsi

Nematoda. *Trichinella* sp. (Prakash and Sharma, 1955)
Arthrocephalus gambiensis Ortlepp (Rao, 1939)
Diserratosomus mungoosei Mirza (1933)
Trematoda. *Paragonius compactus* (Hamerton, 1937)

Herpestes ichneumon

Cestoda. *Hydatigera laticollis parva* Baer (Dollfus, 1962)
Dithyridium elongatum (Blomberg) (Meggitt, 1924b)
Echinococcus granulosus (Batsch) (Meggitt, 1924b)

Herpestes sanguineus

Nematoda. *Rictularia myonacis* Ortlepp (1961)
Travassospirura dentata Monnig (1938)
Filaroides myonaxi Sandground (1937)
Cestoda. *Mathevotaenia herpestes* (Kofend) (Spasskii, 1951)
Mathevotaenia ichneumonitis (Baer) (Spasskii, 1951)

Herpestes smithi

Cestoda. Pleurocercoids (Rewell, 1948)

Atilax paludinosus

Nematoda. *Cloeoascaris spinicollis* Baylis (1923)

Ichneumia albicauda

Cestoda. *Pseudandrya mkuzii* Ortlepp (1963)
Bothricephalus folius (Diesing) (Meggitt, 1924b)
Diphyllobothrium latum (L.) (Meggitt, 1924b)
Taenia herpestis (Setti) (Meggitt, 1924b)

Paracynictis selousi

Cestoda. *Pseudandrya monardi* Fuhrmann (1943)

Cynictis penicillata

Nematoda. *Tenuostrongylus cynictis* Le Roux (1933)

Suricata suricatta

Nematoda. *Ascaris suricattae* Ortlepp (1940)
Numidica suricattae Monnig (1931)
Habronema whitei Monnig (1931)
Microfilaria (Plimmer, 1912)
Cestoda. *Hymenolepis suricattae* Ortlepp (1938)

Arthropods. Mongooses have a large number of arthropod parasites. The Linguatulid, *Armillifer armillatus* Wyman, has been found in *Herpestes naso* and *Crossarchus obscurus* (Hett, 1924). This is a common species in snakes, and its larva has often been found in man. The effect of ticks on the small Indian mongoose in the West Indies has already been noted (p. 69), and Thompson (1950) has listed those that attack the mongoose in Jamaica, which is singularly free of ticks. In Ceylon, *Ixodes ceylonensis* Kohls (1950) is found on *Herpestes smithi.* Many species of lice (Pthiraptera) are found on mongooses. Their specificity and host relations are discussed by Hopkins (1949), who has listed the species known from mongooses. Many species of fleas have also been recorded from mongooses. Population studies of the fleas on *Herpestes auropunctatus* in the Hawaiian islands have been made by Cole & Koepke (1947), Eskey (1934), and Haas (1966). Eskey found four species of fleas on the 1,165 mongooses he examined, including the plague flea, *Xenospylla cheopis.* Haas claims that *H. auropunctatus* is a true host of the cat flea, *Ctenocephalides felis.*

XVII
The kinds of mongooses

THIS chapter is not for reading: it is for reference only. The scientific names of all the different species and subspecies are given together with an account of the distribution of each species. The local or vernacular names of each kind of mongoose are noted where these are known to us.

The family Viverridae includes four subfamilies, the Herpestinae, Viverrinae, Nandiniinae, and Galidictinae. There are 37 genera and about 75 species, most of which are true mongooses (Herpestinae) or genets and civets (Viverrinae). There is only one species of Nandiniinae, *Nandinia binotata* Gray, known as the African palm civet. The Galidictinae include less than a dozen species, all from Madagascar. Many of the Galidictinae and some of the Viverrinae are sometimes called mongooses, but when we speak of mongooses we mean only members of the Herpestinae.

The Viverridae are one of the most generalised families of the order Carnivora. *Herpestes lemanensis* Pomel is known from the Upper Oligocene of France. The genus *Herpestes* has thus been in existence for about 30 million years or longer than any other recent genus in the order Carnivora. Other species of *Herpestes* are known from the Miocene of Spain and from the Pleistocene of the Transvaal. Species of *Mungos*, *Crossarchus*, and *Cynictis* have been described from the Pleistocene of Africa. The last general classification of the Herpestinae is that of Pocock (1919), who then used the name Mungotidae for the group. Eight species of *Herpestes* occur in the Oriental Region, but all other Herpestinae are African and there thus seems to be little doubt that the group is of African origin.

Ten genera of recent Herpestinae are now recognised. These include 36 species. In the following list the genera are arranged from the relatively primitive to the relatively specialised in so far as this can be done in a linear series.

Tribe Herpestini

Herpestes Illiger (1911). Type: *Viverra ichneumon* Linnaeus (1758).
Atilax F. Cuvier (1826). Type: *Herpestes paludinosus* G. Cuvier (1829).
Helogale Gray (1862). Type: *Herpestes parvulus* Sundevall (1846).
Mungos E. Geoffroy & G. Cuvier (1795). Type: *Viverra mungo* Gmelin (1788).
Crossarchus F. Cuvier (1825). Type: *Crossarchus obscurus* F. Cuvier (1825).
Liberiictis Hayman (1958). Type: *Liberiictis kuhni* Hayman (1958).
Dologale Thomas (1926). Type: *Crossarchus dybowski* Pousargues (1893).
Ichneumia I. Geoffroy (1837). Type: *Herpestes albicaudus* G. Cuvier (1929).
Rhynchogale Thomas (1894). Type: *Rhinogale melleri* Gray (1865).
Bdeogale Peters (1850). Type: *Bdeogale crassicauda* Peters (1852).
Paracynictis Pocock (1916). Type: *Cynictis selousi* de Winton (1896).
Cynictis Ogilby (1833). Type: *Herpestes penicillatus* G. Cuvier (1929).

Tribe Suricatini

Suricata Desmarest (1804). Type: *Viverra suricatta* Schreber (1776).

In the list that follows, synonyms have been noted only where it was felt that they would assist the reader in identifying references to the species made in the literature. For instance, the Indian mongoose, *Herpestes edwardsi*, was known as *Mungos mungo* during a period of many years when *Herpestes* was considered to be a synonym of *Mungos*. This is apt to be particularly confusing to the unwary because *Mungos mungo* is now the correct name for a very different kind of mongoose from Africa. In order to make the list easy to use, both the species and subspecies are placed in alphabetical order.

Crossarchus F. Cuvier (1825) is regarded as a subgenus of *Mungos* E. Geoffroy & G. Cuvier (1795) by Ellerman *et al.* (1953), but we have retained it as a distinct genus. *Myonax* Thomas (1928) is a synonym of *Galerella* Gray (1865) as pointed out by Schwarz (1935). *Galerella* is retained as a subgenus of *Herpestes.*

Following Hayman (1940), *Herpestes naso* (de Winton) is removed from the genus *Atilax* in which it was included by Allen (1939) and others. The subspecies and races of *Herpestes brachyurus* are based on Schwarz (1947).

Little regard has been paid to Bechthold's (1939) revision of the Asiatic species of *Herpestes.* He has confounded *H. fuscus* Waterhouse with *H. brachyurus* Gray and *H. auropunctatus* (Hodgson) with *H. javanicus* (Geoffroy). These and other similar mistakes make it difficult to evaluate his apparently new records for the

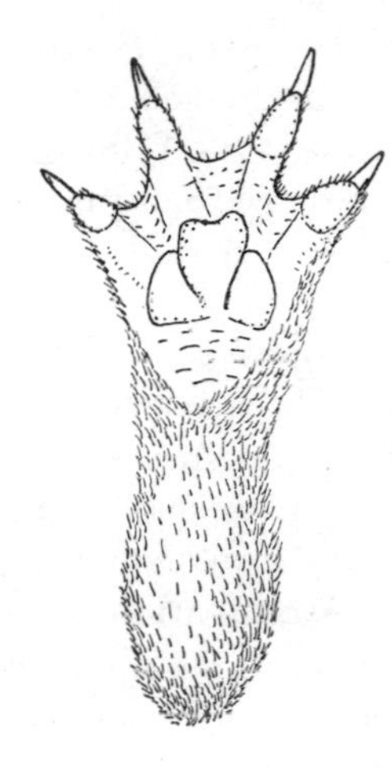

Fig. 25. Right hind foot of *Bdeogale crassicauda*. The genera *Bdeogale*, *Paracynictis*, and *Suricata* have only four toes on both front and hind feet, *Cynictis* has five toes on the front feet and four on the hind feet, but all other mongooses have five toes on both front and hind feet. (After Pocock)

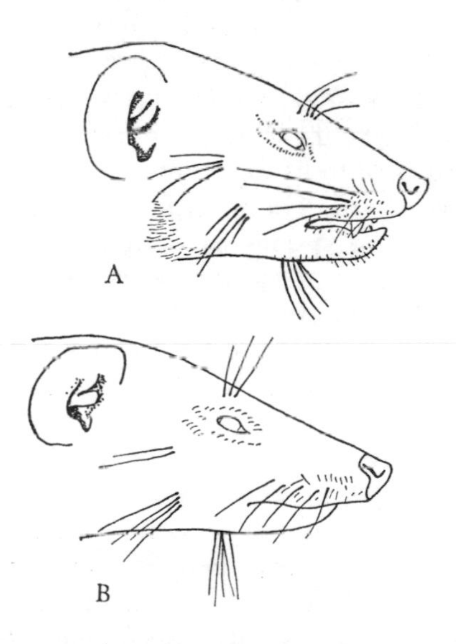

Fig. 26. (A) Head of *Mungos mungo* with ear open. (B) Same of *Crossarchus obscurus*. The vibrissae or sensory hairs of the face are proportionally more slender than they are shown in these and the previous figures of the head. Different kinds of mongooses differ both in the number and length of the vibrissae in the different patches on the face. (After Pocock)

distribution of a number of species. The record of *H. urva* (Hodgson) in Taiwan is based on Bechthold. In their work on the behaviour of the Viverridae, Dücker & Rensch refer to *H. javanicus*. However, there is reason to believe that the species they were using was probably *H. auropunctatus*, and that this confusion is due to their reliance on Bechthold's work.

Following Lundholm (1955), none of the subspecies of *Cynictis penicillata* are recognised. Nevertheless, the subspecies formerly recognised have been listed as synonyms for the assistance of the reader. A study such as that of Lundholm is badly needed in order to establish the status of the very numerous subspecies now recognised of *Herpestes sanguineus*. From a brief examination of the material in the British Museum (Natural History), it would appear that most of the subspecies now recognised are simply seasonal or other types of colour variations: the large number of subspecies that have been described testifies to the industry but not to the discretion of taxonomists, particularly Austin Roberts.

There is no general agreement about the number of valid species of *Helogale* in addition to *H. parvula* (Sundevall). A thorough revision of the genus will almost certainly result in a reduction in the number of species now recognised.

Where it has been possible, we have compiled native names for each species. These lists are clearly far from complete. The only names we have troubled to list are those for which either a locality or a tribe could be given. There would seem to be little value in listing native names for species that range over much of Africa without specifying either the locality in which the name is used or the tribe that uses it. For this reason we have not bothered to record the native names given by some writers, e.g. Walker (1964). Our chief sources of native names were: Allen & Loveridge (1933), Ansell (1960), Frechkop (1943), Matischie (1895), Monad (1935), Pocock (1941), Roberts (1951), and Shortridge (1934).

The number of different kinds of mongooses distinguished by special names by a single tribe is sometimes surprisingly large, and one is left with the disquieting thought that just occasionally the natives invented names to rid themselves of an over zealous questioner. Some of the difficulties in collecting native names may be illustrated by reference to the common mongoose of northern Nigeria. The Hausa name for the animal is *Murida*, but the same animal is sometimes called *Kyanwandaji* to distinguish it from the house cat, *Kyanwangida*: the name for a cat is *Kyanwan*, for bush

Daji, and for a house *Gida*. The other general names for a mongoose in Nigeria are: *Kolokolo* or *Eta* (Yoruba), *Ufu* (Ibo), *Ekiko* (Calabar), and *Ukon* (Ibiobio).

The name mongoose is derived from one of the Indian names for the animal: *mangūs* in Marathi, *manegos* in Tamil (R.L., 1946), *mangusi* in Telegu, *mungasa* in Konkani, and *mungisi* in Canarese. The Portuguese name for the Indian mongoose is *mangus*, the Spanish name is *mangosta*, and the French *mangouste*. In the nineteenth century the English name was sometimes mungoos and sometimes mungoose, but it is now mongoose. According to Rao (1957), remains of the mongoose in or about ruins dating from three to four thousand B.C. indicate that it may have been domesticated in these early times in the Indus valley and the adjoining territories of Sind, Punjab, and Baluchistan.

Atilax paludinosus (G. Cuvier) (1829)

A. p. guineensis Monard (1940)
A. p. macrodon Allen (1924)
A. p. mitis (Thomas & Wroughton) (1903)
A. p. mordax (Thomas) (1912)
A. p. pluto (Temminck) (1853)
A. p. robustus Gray (1865)
A. p. rubellus (Thomas & Wroughton) (1908)
A. p. rubescens (Hollister) (1912)
A. p. spadiceus Cabrera (1921)
A. p. transvaalensis Roberts (1933)

DISTRIBUTION: Most of Africa south of the Sahara; in the west as far north as Portuguese Guinea; in the east in Sudan, Ethiopia, Kenya, Tanzania, Malawi, Zambia, and Mozambique; in the south in Rhodesia, Bechuanaland, and South Africa.

COMMON NAME: Water mongoose.

OTHER NAMES: Marsh mongoose, Grootswart Kommetjiegatmuishond, Kurzschwänzige Mungo, Sumpfichneumon.

NATIVE NAMES: *Nyúndu* (Ovadirico, Ovacuangari, Mambakushu); *Moduba* (Bechuana); *Kambaya* (Sikololo); *Sindondwi* (Chinkoya); *Chitota* (Malavale); *Ká soú si* (Chila); *Slangane*, *Ivugo* (Beira, Inhambane); *Molube* (South Sotho); *Muliza*, *Motswitswi* (Transvaal Sotho); *Ivuzi* (Xhosa, Amaxosa); *Umvuzi* (Zulu); *Iduhwaelimnyama* (Rhodesia Ndebele); *Mkekiua* (Kinya, Kuru); *Khakhakha* (Nyanja); *Mukala* (Lozi); *Shinkeke* (Kaondi). Ghana: *Dompo* (Fanti, Bron, Wassaw); *Odompo* (Twi, Ashanti, Lelemi, Nkonya); *Kabi* (Sefwi); *Kaabi* (Brissa); *Kelungbo* (Nzima); *Odonkpo* (Ga); *Kukpa* (Bowiri); *Kadompo* (Akpafo).

Bdeogale (Bdeogale) crassicauda Peters (1852)

B. c. omnivora Heller (1913)
B. c. puisa Peters (1852)
B. c. tenuis Thomas & Wroughton (1908)
DISTRIBUTION: Kenya, Tanzania, Mozambique.
COMMON NAME: Four-toed mongoose.
OTHER NAMES: Bushy-tailed mongoose, Bushy-tailed meerkat, Dikstert-muishond.

Bdeogale (Galeriscus) nigripes Pucheran (1855)

B. n. jacksoni Thomas (1894)
DISTRIBUTION: Kenya, Gabon.
COMMON NAME: Black-footed mongoose.

Crossarchus alexandri Thomas & Wroughton (1907)

DISTRIBUTION: Congo.

Crossarchus ansorgei Thomas (1910)

DISTRIBUTION: Congo, north-western Angola.
COMMON NAME: Angolan Kusimanse.

Crossarchus obscurus F. Cuvier (1825)

DISTRIBUTION: West Africa from Portuguese Guinea to Gabon.
COMMON NAME: Kusimanse or Cusimanse.
NATIVE NAMES: Ghana: *Ahweaa* (Twi, Ashanti); *Ahweaa Biri* (Bron); *Aŭisa* (Wassaw); *Awonzoi* (Sefwi, Brissa); *Avisea* (Nzima); *Ahwea* (Bowiri, Lelemi); *Wia* (Nkonya); Mayagyiga (Dompo).

Cynictis penicillata (G. Cuvier) (1829)

SYNONYMS formerly regarded as subspecies: *bechuanae* Roberts (1932), *brachyura* Roberts (1924), *bradfieldi* Roberts (1924), *cinderella* Thomas (1927), *coombsi* Roberts (1929), *intensa* Schwann (1906), *kalaharica* Roberts (1932), *karasensis* Roberts (1938), *leptura* Smith (1839), *ogilbyi* (Smith) (1834), *pallidior* Thomas & Schwann (1904).
DISTRIBUTION: South Africa, South West Africa, Southern Angola, Bechuanaland.
COMMON NAME: Yellow mongoose.
OTHER NAMES: Red meerkat, Bushy-tailed meerkat, Geelmeerkat, Rooimeerkat.
NATIVE NAMES: *Erupúka-okarúmbu* (Herero); *Halúni* (Ovambo); *Motódi*, *Móasha* (Bechuana); *|Hei|e:b*, *Heixarab*, *|Awa|eeb*, *Hcryki*, *Horyki* (Nama Hottentot); *|Awa|areb* (Hei||kum Bushman); *Tsẽ* (||*K'au*||en Bushman); ǂ*Ga:wub*, *Tshamgaba* (Naron Bushman); *Awa areb* (Hei kum Bushman); !*Gei* (||Ng!ke Bushman); |*Q* (|Auni Bushman); *Xara* (|Kam-ha! ke Bushman); *Igala* (Xhosa); *Mosha* (South Sotho); *Pipi* (Transvaal Sotho).

Dologale dybowski (Pousargues) (1893)

DISTRIBUTION: Congo, Sudan.

Helogale hirtula Thomas (1904)

H. h. ahlselli Lönnberg (1912)
H. h. annulata Drake-Brockman (1912)
H. h. lutescens Thomas (1911)
H. h. powelli Drake-Brockman (1912)
DISTRIBUTION: Ethiopia, Somalia, Kenya.

Helogale ivori Thomas (1919)

DISTRIBUTION: Mozambique.

Helogale macmillani Thomas (1906)

DISTRIBUTION: Ethiopia.

Helogale parvula (Sundevall) (1846)

SYNONYM: *H. brunnula* Thomas & Schwann (1906)
H. p. (?) *affinis* Hollister (1916). Status uncertain.
H. p. (?) *atkinsoni* Thomas (1897). Status uncertain.
H. p. mimetra Thomas (1926)
SYNONYM: *H. p. brunetta* Thomas (1926)
H. p. nero Thomas (1926)
SYNONYM: *H. p. bradfieldi* Roberts (1928)
H. p. ruficeps Kershaw (1922)
H. p. (?) *rufula* Thomas (1910). Status uncertain.
H. p. undulata (Peters) (1852)
DISTRIBUTION: South Africa, South West Africa, Angola, Bechuanaland, Rhodesia, Mozambique, Zambia, Malawi, Congo, Tanzania, Kenya, Ethiopia, Somalia.
COMMON NAME: Dwarf mongoose.
OTHER NAMES: Small brown mongoose, Wahlberg's mongoose, Dwerg-muishond, Zwerg-Manguste.
NATIVE NAMES: *Erupúka-umquaslni* (Herero); ! *Ãxareb* (Nama Hottentot); *Mwili*, *Usisikwi* (Sikololo); *Mukungilia* (Chinkoya); *Kamali* (Tonga); *Mwile*, *Mwite* (Chilavale); *Matushi* (Mashasha); *Mahlwe* (Tsonga); *Matswi* (Venda); *Nyashane* (Zulu); *Isidyororo* (Karanga); *Motswitswane* (Transvaal Sotho); *Ubutluli* ?, *Ubuthwethwe* ? (Rhodesia Ndebele); *Kitafe* (Swahili); *Viquiri* (Usagara); *Ndjororo* (Usambiri); *Kandjororo* (Kissukuma); *Kanjamukori* (Kitusi); *Chikolokolo* (Kaundi); *Omukondo*, *Tyimwéné* (Angola).

Helogale percivali Thomas (1911)

H. p. tenebrosa Lönnberg (1918)
DISTRIBUTION: Kenya.

Helogale varia Thomas (1902)

DISTRIBUTION: Malawi.

Helogale vetula Thomas (1911)

DISTRIBUTION: Kenya.

Helogale victorina Thomas (1902)

H. v. ochracea Thomas (1910)
DISTRIBUTION: Kenya, Uganda, Tanzania.
NATIVE NAME: *Sala* (Chigogo).

Herpestes (Herpestes) auropunctatus (Hodgson) (1836)

H. a. birmanicus Thomas (1886)
H. a. pallipes (Blyth) (1845)
SYNONYM: *H. persicus* Gray (1864)
H. a. rubrifrons (Allen) (1909)
H. a. siamensis (Kloss) (1917)
H. a. palustris Ghose (1965). Status uncertain.
DISTRIBUTION: Iraq, Persia, Arabia, Afghanistan, Kashmir, India south to Sind on the west and Orissa on the east, Nepal, Burma, Siam, Malay Peninsula, South China, Hainan. Introduced and established in Mafia Island (Tanzania), the Hawaiian Islands, and the Caribbean. In the West Indies it is on all of the larger islands: Cuba, Jamaica, Hispaniola, Puerto Rico, and Trinidad. In the Virgin Islands it is on St Croix, Buck, Vieques, St Thomas, St John, and Tortola but not on Virgin Gordo, Culebra, Jost Van Dyke, and Anegada. In the Leeward Islands it is on St Kitts, Nevis, Antiqua, Guadeloupe, Marie Galante, and almost certainly on Désirade, but it is absent on Saba, St Eustatius, and Dominica. We have not discovered whether it is present on the larger remaining islands of the group, that is, Sombrero, Anguilla, St Martin, St Bathélemy, Barbuda, and Redonda. In the Windward Islands it is on Martinique, St Lucia, St Vincent, Barbados, and Grenada, but it does not appear to be present on any of the Grenadines. It is also absent on Tobago. On the mainland it is established in the coastal areas of British Guiana, Surinam, and French Guiana.
COMMON NAME: Small Indian mongoose.
OTHER NAMES: Gold-speckled mongoose, Javan golden-brown mongoose, Small yellow mongoose, Pale-footed mongoose.
NATIVE NAMES: *Núl* (Kashmir); *Mwe-ba* (Burma); *Mush-i-Khourma* (Persia); *Ueraydee ma'l Nhakala* or *Abu al arrais* (Arabic).

Herpestes (Urva) brachyurus Gray (1936)

H. b. brachyurus Gray (=*H. semitorquatus uniformis* Robinson & Kloss, 1919)
RACE: *H. b. sumatrius* Thomas (1921). Sumatra.
RACE: *H. b. javanensis* Bechthold (1936). Malay Peninsula, Java, Sumatra.

H. b. semitorquatus Gray (1846)

RACE: *H. b. hosei* Jentik (1903). Sarawak.

RACE: *H. b. rajah* Thomas (1921). Sarawak.

RACE: *H. b. dyacorum* Thomas (1940). Borneo.

DISTRIBUTION: Malay Peninsula, Sumatra, Java, Borneo, Sarawak, Palawan.

COMMON NAME: Malay short-tailed mongoose.

Herpestes (Herpestes) edwardsi (Geoffroy) (1812)

SYNONYMS: *Ichneumon griseus* Geoffroy (1812) or *Herpestes griseus*; *Mungos mungo* (Blanford) (1888) or *Herpestes mungo*.

H. e. ferrugineus Blanford (1874)

H. e. lanka (Wroughton) (1915)

H. e. nyula (Hodgson) (1836)

DISTRIBUTION: Persia, Iraq, Arabia, Afghanistan, Pakistan, India, Ceylon, Nepal, Assam. Introduced into Malaya (Chasen, 1940), Mauritius, and Ryukyu and Tonaki Islands.

COMMON NAME: Indian mongoose.

OTHER NAMES: Common Indian mongoose, Common grey mongoose, Indian grey mongoose, Common Bengal mongoose.

NATIVE NAMES: *Mangús*, *Mungus* (Marathi, Dekhani); *Múngali*, *Mungili* (Kanarese); *Yentawa*, *Mangisa* (Telegu); *Múngsi*, *Antúr* (Waddari, Haran Shikaris); *Kera Hon-Kera* (Coorg); *Koral* (Gond); *Beji* (Bengal); *Newal*, *Newala*, *Newul*, *Neul*, *Nyul*, *Newar*, *Dhor*, *Rasu* (Hindi); *Nurlia* (Kathiawar); *Binquidaro*, *Sarambumbui* (Ho Kol); *Mugatiya*, *Moogatea* (Sinhalese); *Kiri*, *Kiripulle*, *Karupa Keeri* (Tamil); *Keerie* (Jaffna Tamil); *Yerkopegi* (Turkish).

Herpestes (Herpestes) fuscus Waterhouse (1838)

H. f. flavidens Kelaart (1850)

SYNONYMS: *H. ceylanicus* Nevill (1887 ?); *H. f. ceylonicus* Thomas (1924)

H. f. maccarthiae (Gray) (1851)

H. f. rubidor Pocock (1937)

H. f. siccatus Thomas (1924)

DISTRIBUTION: Southern India, Ceylon.

COMMON NAME: Indian brown mongoose.

OTHER NAMES: Brown mongoose, Ceylon brown mongoose, Nilgherry brown mongoose.

NATIVE NAMES: *Sendali-Kera* (Coorg); *Mugatiya*, *Ram-mugatiya* (Sinhalese); *Kiri-pulle*, *Karrang-Kiri*, *Poo-Kiri*, *Pambu-Kiri* (Tamil).

Herpestes (Herpestes) ichneumon (Linnaeus) (1758)

SYNONYMS: *Ichneumon aegyptiae* Tiedemann (1809), *Ichneumon major* E. Geoffroy (1812), *Ichneumon pharaon* Lacepede (1799).

H. i. angolensis Bocage (1890)

H. i. cafer (Gmelin) (1788)

H. i. centralis (Lönnberg) (1917)

H. i. funestus (Osgood) (1910)
H. i. mababiensis Roberts (1932)
H. i. numidicus (F. Cuvier) (1834)
H. i. occidentalis Monard (1940)
H. i. parvidens (Lönnberg) (1908)
H. i. sabiensis Roberts (1926)
H. i. sangronizi Cabrera (1924)
H. i. widdringtoni Gray (1842)

DISTRIBUTION: Spain, Portugal, Israel, and most of Africa, e.g. Morocco, Algeria, Egypt, Sudan, Ethiopia, Somalia, Malawi, Congo, Zambia, Mozambique, South Africa into Cape Province, Angola, Nigeria, and Portuguese Guinea. Introduced into Madagascar and Italy.

COMMON NAME: Ichneumon.

OTHER NAMES: Egyptian ichneumon, Egyptian mongoose, Large grey mongoose, Cape ichneumon, Groot Grysmuishond, Vaalmuishond, or Vaal Kommetjiegatmuishond, Kot Pharoon or Pharoah's cat, Tiffeh.

NATIVE NAMES: *Nems*, *Nims*, *Nymss* (Coptic); *Serro* (Arabic amongst Moors); *Mukéngi* (Ovadirico, Ovacuangari, Mambakushu); *Gwegara*, *Gwegala* (Mambakushu-Simbukushu); *Mukala-wa-lilangu*, *Mikala*, *Mukata* (Sikololo); *Mukala* (Chila); *Mukulanga* (Chinkoya); *Kawusanga*, *Kausanga* (Tonga ?); *Umhlangala*, *Ilitse* (Xhosa); *Umvunti* (Swahili); *Umhlangala*, *Ushonga* (Zulu); *Uwobo* (Rhodesia Ndebele); *Nyeretzi* (Kikinga); *Nyenga* (Nyanja); *Mukengé* (Kaondi, Ngangela); *Buhunga* (Kikunde); *Umuyongwe*, *Muderere* (Kiniaruanda).

Herpestes (Herpestes) javanicus (Geoffroy) (1812)

H. j. exilis Gervais (1841)
SYNONYM: *H. rutilus* Gray (1861)
H. j. orientalis Soddy (1936)
H. j. peninsulae (Schwarz) (1910)
H. j. rafflesii Anderson (1875)
H. j. tjerapai Soddy (1949)

DISTRIBUTION: Malay Peninsula, Java, Sumatra, Siam, Cambodia, Vietnam.

COMMON NAME: Javan mongoose.

NATIVE NAME: *Garangan* (Java).

Herpestes (Herpestes) naso de Winton (1901)

SYNONYM: *Xenogale microdon* Allen (1919)
H. n. almodovari Cabrera (1903)
H. n. nigerianus (Thomas) (1912)

DISTRIBUTION: Sierra Leone, Ghana, Nigeria, Cameroon, Congo.

Herpestes (Galerella) ochracea Gray (1849)

H. o. fulvidior Thomas (1904)
H. o. perfulvida Thomas (1904)

DISTRIBUTION: Ethiopia, Somalia.

NATIVE NAME: *Sorgur* (Somali).

Herpestes (Galerella) pulverulentus Wagner (1839)

SYNONYMS: A reddish variety *H. p. shortridgei* (Roberts) (1932) and a black variety *H. p. nigratus* (Thomas) (1928). The latter variety and *Helogale p. nero* are the only two black mongooses in southern Africa. The Kaokoveld natives have the same name in Herero for the two because they believe that *Helogale p. nero* is the immature form of *H. p. nigratus.*

H. p. annulatus Lundholm (1955)
H. p. basuticus (Roberts) (1936)
H. p. ruddi Thomas (1903)

DISTRIBUTION: South and South West Africa. Cape of Good Hope to Orange Free State and Basutoland; in west from the Cape to the Angolan border.

COMMON NAME: Cape grey mongoose.

OTHER NAMES: Cape lesser grey mongoose, Small grey mongoose, Klein Grysmuishond, Klein Gryskommetjiegatmuishond. The variety *nigratus* is known as the Black mongoose, Black slender mongoose, or Swartmuishond. The variety *shortridgei* is known as the Cunene red mongoose or Kunene-rooimuishond. The subspecies *ruddi* is Rudd's mongoose or Rudd Muishond.

NATIVE NAMES: *Erupúka-umquasíni* (Herero) for *nigratus*, *Erupuka-mona* (Herero) and *Hamwhiri* (Ovambo) for *shortridgei*; *T'ceep* (Nama Hottentot) for the subspecies *ruddi*; and *Ilitse Unomatse* (Xhosa) and *Mochalla* (South Sotho) for the typical subspecies.

Herpestes (Galerella) sanguineus Rüppell (1836)

H. s. auratus (Thomas & Wroughton) (1908)
H. s. bocagei Thomas & Wroughton (1905)
H. s. bradfieldi (Roberts) (1932)
H. s. caldatus Thomas (1927)
H. s. canus (Wroughton) (1907)
H. s. cauui (Smith) (1836)
H. s. dasilvai (Roberts) (1938)
H. s. dentifer (Heller) (1913)
H. s. erongensis (Roberts) (1946)
H. s. flavescens Bocage (1889)
H. s. galbus (Wroughton) (1909)
H. s. gracilis Rüppell (1836)
H. s. grantii (Gray) (1865)
H. s. ibeae (Wroughton) (1907)
H. s. ignitoides (Roberts) (1932)
H. s. ignitus (Roberts) (1913)
H. s. kalaharicus (Roberts) (1932)
H. s. kaokoensis (Roberts) (1932)
H. s. karasensis (Roberts) (1938)
H. s. lancasteri (Roberts) (1932)
H. s. melanurus (Martin) (1836)
H. s. mossambicus (Matschie) (1914)
H. s. mustela (Schwarz) (1935)

H. s. mutgigella Rüppell (1836)
H. s. ngamiensis (Roberts) (1932)
H. s. okavangensis (Roberts) (1932)
H. s. orestes (Heller) (1911)
H. s. ornatus Peters (1852)
H. s. parvipes (Hollister) (1916)
H. s. phoenicurus (Thomas) (1907)
H. s. proteus (Thomas) (1907)
H. s. punctulatus Gray (1849)
H. s. ratlamuchi (Smith) (1836)
H. s. rendilis (Lönnberg) (1912)
H. s. rufescens Lorenz (1898)
H. s. saharae Thomas (1925)
H. s. swalius Thomas (1927)
H. s. swinnyi (Roberts) (1913)
H. s. ugandae (Wroughton) (1909)
H. s. upingtoni (Shortridge) (1934)
H. s. zombae (Wroughton) (1907)

DISTRIBUTION: Most of Africa south of the Sahara; in the west from Senegal, Sierra Leone, Nigeria, Cameroon, and Angola through South Africa to the Cape; in the east in Sudan, Ethiopia, Somalia, Uganda, Kenya, Tanzania, Malawi, Mozambique, Zambia, and Rhodesia.

COMMON NAME: Slender mongoose.

OTHER NAMES: Ruddy mongoose, Bechuana red mongoose, Zambesi red mongoose, Fiery-red mongoose, Transvaal slender mongoose, Black-tipped mongoose, Dwust mongoose, Rooimuishond, Transvaalse Rooimuishond, Sambesi Rooimuishond, Betsoeanalandse Rooimuishond, Vuurrooimuishond.

NATIVE NAMES: *Erupúka-kumugúési* (Herero); *Hamwhíri* (Ovambo); *Khánu*, *Móäsha*, *Mosi* (Bechuana); *Kamghóno* (Mambakushu); *Kamungkóndo* (Ovadirico, Ovacuangari); *|A:wa|e:b* (Berg Damara); *|A:wa:|e:b*, *ǂNu:|e:b* (Nama Hottentot); *Tsõa:ni:sa* (||K'au||en & !Kung Bushman); *Tsa|noë* (Naron Bushman); *Kambwinji* (Sikololo); *Mumbuluma*, *Mugondo-wa-mushia-ku-shipa* (Chinkoya); *Mukongo* (Chilavale); *Kamale*, *Lukobo* (Tonga); *Luchende* (Chila); *Mumbuluma* (Kaonde); *Mutoso* (?) (Mashasha); *Gorogoro* (Nyanja); *Uchakide*, *Ubhoshobana*, *Umbonjolo* (Zulu); *Uchakidze* (?) (Swahili); *Ubuchakidi* (Rhodesia Ndebele); *Mangoro* (Tsonga); *Kganwe*, *Kgano* (Tswana); *Kgano* (Transvaal Sotho); *Lukhohe* (Venda); *Runkoe* (Tete); *Kihindi* (Kihele); *Lukwiru* (Kihehe); *Ipulu* (Bemba); *Likongwe* (Nyunja); *Kangondo* (Lozi); *Mumbuluma* (Kaondi); *Busisi*, *Kayongwe* (Belgian Congo). *Kamukondo* (Ngangela), *Karili* (Kalukembé). Ghana: *Kokobo* (Fanti, Twi, Ashanti, Bron, Wassaw, Nzima, Ga, Adanbe-Krobo, Ewe, Bowiri, Lelemi, Banda-Ashanti, Meantra, Wangara, Gyoro, Dompo); *Kokobe* (Fanti); *Panyinmmisa* (Ashanti); *Asefoboa* (Sefwi, Brissa); *Tukpete* (Akpafo); *Okpakayo* (Nkonya); *Solo* (Gyimini); *Süta* (Mo); *Sisol* (Lobi).

Herpestes (Herpestes) smithi Gray (1837)

H. s. zeylanius Thomas (1921)

DISTRIBUTION: India from Rajputana east to Bengal and south through the Eastern and Western Ghats into Ceylon.

COMMON NAME: Ruddy mongoose or Long-tailed mongoose.

NATIVE NAMES: *Konda Yentava* (Telegu); *Hötamba, Deeto* (Sinhalese); *Kiri* or *Seng-Kiri* (Tamil); *Seng-Keerie* or *Raja-Keerie* (Jaffna Tamil).

Herpestes (Urva) urva (Hodgson) (1836)

SYNONYM: *H. cancrivora* (Hodgson) (1837)

DISTRIBUTION: Nepal, Assam, Burma, Thailand, Vietnam, South China, Hainan, Taiwan.

COMMON NAME: Crab-eating mongoose.

NATIVE NAMES: *Arava* (Nepal); *Mwe-ba* (Burma).

Herpestes (Urva) vitticollis Bennett (1835)

H. v. inornatus Pocock (1941)

DISTRIBUTION: Southern India, Ceylon.

COMMON NAME: Striped-necked mongoose.

NATIVE NAMES: *Quoki Balu, Kati Kera* (Coorg); *Gal-Mugatiya, Locu-Mugatyia, Loco-Moogatea* (Sinhalese); *Malam Kiri* (Tamil).

Ichneumia albicauda (G. Cuvier) (1829)

I. a. dialeucos (Hollister) (1916)

I. a. grandis (Thomas) (1889)

SYNONYM: *I. a. haagneri* Roberts (1924)

I. a. ibeana (Thomas) (1904)

I. a. loandae (Thomas) (1904)

I. a. loempo (Temminck) (1853)

DISTRIBUTION: Southern Arabia as far as Muscat. Most of Africa south of the Sahara; Sudan, Ethiopia, Somalia, Uganda, Congo, Kenya, Tanzania, Malawi, Mozambique, Zambia, Rhodesia, and Transvaal; in the west from Senegal, Portuguese Guinea, Ghana, Nigeria, and Angola to South Africa as far as Cape Province.

COMMON NAME: White-tailed mongoose or Witstertmuishond.

NATIVE NAMES: *Arutondo* ? (Ovadirico, Ovacuangari, Mambakushu); *Nkema, Nkeyema* (Sikololo); *Nchema, Muchema* (Chila); *Kiyema* (Chinkoya); *Keyema* (Chilavale); *Nkema* (Ntonga); *Iduhwa, Iduhwa-elimnyama* (Rhodesia Ndebele); *Sanganyi, Tlolota* (Tsonga); *Ingqwalashu* (Xhosa); *Igqalashu, Iqalashu* (Zulu); *Mutsherere* (Venda); *Motôpa* (Transvaal Sotho); *Saka* (Kinyaturu); *Kananga* (Kikami); *Silutuba* (Tonga); *Nkeyema* (Lozi); *Nkema* (Kaondi); *Kitende* (Kiniaruanda); *Kicheche, Nguchiro* (Kiswahili); *Linenga* (Angola).

Liberiictis kuhni Hayman (1958)

DISTRIBUTION: Liberia.

NATIVE NAME: *Boire-senna.*

Mungos gambianus (Ogilby) (1835)

DISTRIBUTION: Gambia.

COMMON NAME: Gambian mongoose.

NATIVE NAMES: Ghana: *Ahweaa* (Bron); *Nyankikyo* (Gonja); *Afirigya* (Banda-Wasifu); *Firigyaa* (Banda-Ashanti, Gyoro); *Figya* (Meantra); *Kanzoliwata* (Wangara); *Gyimini* (Gyimini); *Nyaawuro* (Dompo); *Mayagyiga* (Mo); *Sisol* (Lobi); *Tubaya* (Kusasi, Dagomba).

Mungos mungo (Gmelin) (1788)

M. m. bororensis Roberts (1929)
M. m. caurinus Thomas (1926)
M. m. colonus (Heller) (1911)
M. m. damarensis Zukowsky (1956)
M. m. gothneh (Heuglin & Fitzinger) (1866)
M. m. grisonax Thomas (1926)
M. m. macrurus (Thomas) (1907)
M. m. mandjarum (Schwarz) (1915)
M. m. ngamiensis Roberts (1932)
M. m. pallidipes Roberts (1929)
M. m. rossi Roberts (1929)
M. m. senescens (Thomas & Wroughton) (1907)
M. m. somalicus (Thomas) (1895)
M. m. talboti (Thomas & Wroughton) (1908)
M. m. zebra (Rüppell) (1835)
M. m. zebroides (Lönnberg) (1908)

DISTRIBUTION: West Africa from Portuguese Guinea, Nigeria, Cameroon, and Angola to South Africa as far as Cape Province; Sudan, Ethiopia, Somalia, Uganda, Kenya, Congo, Malawi, Mozambique, Rhodesia, Bechuanaland, and Transvaal.

COMMON NAME: Banded mongoose.

OTHER NAMES: Gebandemuishond, Gestrepte Kommetjiegatmuishond, Zebra-Manguste.

NATIVE NAMES: *Erupúka-otúta* (Herero); *Onghára, Mkúndakunda* (Ovambo); *Lutotóhto, Letototo* (Bechuana); *Karangkára* (Ovadirico, Ovacuangari); *Kapurāȳ* (Mambakushu); *Niexarab* (Nama Hottentot, Berg Damara); *Nei|areb* (Hei||kum Bushman); *!Gaë* (! Kung Bushman); *Gĩ:se* (||K'au||en Bushman); *Daũxarasi* (Naron Bushman); *Kangalanyake, Kanalanyake* (Sikololo); *Kala* (Chilavale); *Sikapulwe* (Chila, Tonga); *Ubuhala, Ubuhaye, Uguya* (Zulu); *Moswe* (Transvaal Sotho); *Nkala* (Tsonga); *Tshihoho* (Venda); *Madenbo* (Beira); *Ndembo* (Gorongoza, Tete); *Nkala* (Kiskuma); *Limkalla* (Kinyamwesi); *Gitschiro* (Kisuahili); *Goozeero* (Ukuni); *Musulu* (Nyanja); *Mapulwe* (Tonga); *Pifo* (Lozi); *Nakula* (Kaondi); *Ikorwe* (Kiniaruanda); *Kalankala* (Angola); *Shug-shug* (Somali).

Paracynictis selousi (de Winton) (1896)

P. s. bechuanae Roberts (1932)
P. s. ngamiensis Roberts (1932)
P. s. sengaani Roberts (1931)

DISTRIBUTION: South Africa, South West Africa, Angola, Malawi, Zambia, and Rhodesia.

COMMON NAME: Selous' mongoose.

OTHER NAMES: Selous' meerkat, Selouse meerkat, Kleinwitstertmuishond.

NATIVE NAMES: *Pifu Pifo* (Sikololo); *Skakamalala, Silumba* (Chila); *Luhama* (Chinkoya); *Luama* (Matotela); *Sangwi* (Chilavale); *Silimba, Momba* (Tonga); *Insengane* (Zulu); *Iduhwa* (Rhodesia Ndebele); *Manhauta* (Transvaal Sotho); *Kahama* (Kaondi); *Kahangu* (Lozi).

Rhynchogale melleri (Gray) (1865)

R. m. caniceps Kershaw (1924)

R. m. langi Roberts (1938)

DISTRIBUTION: Tanzania, Malawi, Zambia, Rhodesia, Mozambique, Swaziland, Transvaal, Natal.

COMMON NAME: Meller's mongoose or Mellerse Muishond.

NATIVE NAMES: *Nauuwala* (Barotse); *Mchema* (Chila); *Chimpumpi* (Kaondi); *Kafundi* (Lozi).

Suricata suricatta (Schreber) (1776)

SYNONYMS: *S. s. hahni* Thomas (1927); *S. s. hamiltoni* Thomas & Schwann (1905); *S. s. lophurus* Thomas & Schwann (1905); *S. s. namaquensis* Thomas & Schwann (1905).

S. s. marjoriae Bradfield (1935)

DISTRIBUTION: South and South West Africa.

COMMON NAME: Meerkat.

OTHER NAMES: Suricate, Grey meerkat, Slender-tailed meerkat, Graatjiemierkat, Stokstertmierkat.

NATIVE NAMES: *Erupúka-umkúndakúnda* (Herero); *Lesiĕ* (Bechuana); ǂ*Ui*ǂ*ui:seb* (Nama Hottentot, Berg Damara); *Hcryky* (Nama Hottentot of Little Namaqualand); Xarab, Dzwõa (||K'au||en Bushman); *Xara:gï, Nauba* (Naron Bushman); ||*Nau* (|Nu||en Bushman); ǂ*Nwa* (|Auni Bushman); *Kunsi* (||Ng!ke Bushman); !*Kao* (|Kam-ha!ke Bushman); *Letoli* (South Sotho); *Letototo, Motototo* (Transvaal Sotho); *Cagiti* (Zulu, Transvaal).

References

THE following list includes only those books and articles to which reference has been made in the text. Some of the original references have not been verified, and their contents are known to us only from other sources: all of these are indicated by an asterisk.

Adams, E. G. P. (1931). The striped-necked mongoose (*Herpestes vitticollis*). *J. Bombay nat. Hist. Soc.* **34**, 1054.

Adie, A. J. (1829). Notice of the habits of a mangouste kept in Canaan Cottage, near Edinburg. *Ann. Mag. nat. Hist.* **1**, 20-22.

Alexander, A. D., Benenson, A. S., Byrne, R. J., Diaz-Rivera, R. S., Evans, L. B., Grochenour, W., Hall, H. E., Hightower, J. A., Jeffries, H., de Jesus, J., Martinez, E., Paniagua, M., Pons, A., Ramos-Morales, F., Rodriguez-Molina, R., Swisher, K. Y., Woodward, T. E., and Yager, R. H. (1963). Leptospirosis in Puerto Rico. *Zoonoses Res.* **2**, 153-227.

Alexander, A. J. (1958). On the stridulation of scorpions. *Behaviour* **12**, 339-52.

*Alicata, J. E. (1944). A study of leptospirosis in Hawaii. *Plantat. Health* (*Aiea, Oahu, T. H.*) **8** (4), 6-33

*Alicata, J. E., and Breaks, V. (1943). A survey of leptospirosis in Honolulu. *Hawaii med. J.* **2**, 137-42.

Allen, G. M. (1911). Mammals of the West Indies. *Bull. Mus. comp. Zool. Harv.* **54**, 175-263.

Allen, G. M. (1939). Checklist of African mammals. *Bull. Mus. comp. Zool. Harv.* **83**, 1-763.

Allen, G. M., and Loveridge, A. (1933). Reports on the scientific results of an expedition to the south western highlands of Tanganyika Territory. *Bull. Mus. comp. Zool. Harv.* **75**, 47-140.

Anderson, J. (1902). *Zoology of Egypt*: *Mammalia* (revised and completed by W. E. de Winton). London. Hugh Rees.

Anonymous (1897a). Ticks and mongoose. *J. Inst. Jamaica* **2**, 471.

Anonymous (1897b). The Indian mongoose in Jamaica. *J. Bombay nat. Hist. Soc.* **11**, 161-2.

Anonymous (1918a). The mongoose. *Proc. agric. Soc. Trin. Tob.* **18**, 603-30.

Anonymous (1918b). Rats and mongoose in the West Indies. *Bull. Dep. Agric. Trin. Tob.* **17**, 187-90.

Anonymous (1918c). Mongoose ordinance 1918. *Bull. Dep. Agric. Trin. Tob.* **17**, 190-2.

Anonymous (1936). The domesticated mongoose: 'Rikki'—home pet and film star. *Ill. Lond. News* **189**, 876-7.

Anonymous (1946). The mongoose in Australia. *Vict. Nat., Melb.* **62**, 205.

Ansell, W. F. H. (1960). *Mammals of Northern Rhodesia.* Lusaka.

Baldwin, P. H., Schwartz, C. W., and Schwarz, E. R. (1952). Life history and economic status of the mongoose in Hawaii. *J. Mammal.* **33**, 335-56.

Barbour, T. (1930). Some faunistic changes in the Lesser Antilles. *Proc. New Engl. zool. Cl.* **11**, 73-85.

Barnum, C. C. (1930). Rat control in Hawaii. *Hawaii. Plant. Rec.* **34**, 421-43.

Barrett-Hamilton, G. E. H., and Hinton, M. A. C. (1916). *A history of British mammals.* Parts XVIII & XIX.

Baylis, H. A. (1923). A new Ascarid from an otter. *Ann. Mag. nat. Hist.* (9) **11**, 459-63.

Bechthold, G. (1939). Die asiatischen Formen der Gattung *Herpestes. Z. Saugetierk.* **14**, 113-219.

Beddard, F. E. (1909). Mammalis. In *The Cambridge Natural History.* London. Macmillan & Co.

Beebe, W. (1922). *The Edge of the Jungle.* London.

Blanford, W. T. (1888). *The fauna of British India including Ceylon and Burma. Mammalia.* **1**. London. Taylor & Francis.

Boessneck, J. (1953). Die Haustiere in Altägypten. *Veröff. zool. Staats-samml. Münch.* **3**, 1-50.

Brownlow, A. L'E. (1940a). How the mongoose counteracts snake bite. *J. Bombay nat. Hist. Soc.* **42**, 183.

Brownlow, A. L'E. (1940b). Crab-eating mongoose (*Herpestes urva* (Hodgs.)) in captivity. *J. Bombay nat. Hist. Soc.* **41**, 893-4.

Bruijns, M. F. M. (1961). Over vogel bescherming, mangoestes en beren in Italie. *Levende Nat.* **64**, 61-64.

Brunner-Traut, E. (1965). Spitzmaus und Ichneumon als Tiere des Sonnengottes. *Nachr. Akad. Wiss. Gottingen* (*Phil.-Hist. Klasse*) **1965**, 123-63.

Bryan, W. A. (1908). Some birds of Molokai. *Occ. Pap. Bishop Mus.* **4**, 133-76.

*Buytendijk, F. J. J. (1932). *Reaktionzeit und Schlagfertigkeit.* Kassel. Rudolf & Meister.

*Buytendijk, F. J. J. (1952). *Traité de psychologie animale.* University of France Press.

Calmette, A. (1898). Inoculation against the venom of snakes and the new treatment of venomous bites. *J. Bombay nat. Hist. Soc.* **11**, 515-625.

Calmette, A. (1907). *Les venins.* Paris.

Cansdale, G. S. (1946). *Animals of West Africa.* London. Longmans, Green, & Co.

Cansdale, G. S. (1952). *Animals and man.* London. Hutchinson.

Chasen, F. N. (1940). A handlist of Malaysian mammals. A systematic list of the mammals of the Malay Peninsula, Sumatra, Borneo and Java, including the adjacent small islands. *Bull. Raffles Mus.* **15**, 1-209.

Chatin, J. (1874). Recherches pour servir a l'histoire anatomique des glandes odorantes des mammifères (Carnassiers et rongeurs). *Ann. sci. Nat.* (5) **19**, 1-135.

Cheesman, R. E. (1920). Report on the mammals of Mesopotamia collected by members of the Mesopotamian expeditionary force, 1915 to 1919. *J. Bombay nat. Hist. Soc.* **27**, 323-46.

Clark, A. H. (1905). Birds of the southern Lesser Antilles. *Proc. Boston Soc. nat. Hist.* **32**, 203-312.

Cluver, E. (1927). Rabies in South Africa. *J. med. Ass. S. Afr.* **1**, 247-53.

Cole, L. C., and Koepke, J. A. (1947). A study of rodent ectoparasites in Honolulu. *Publ. Hlth Rep., Wash.* (*Suppl.*) **202**, 25-41.

*Colon, E. D. (1930). *Datos sobre la historia de la agricultura de Puerto Rico antes* 1898. San Juan, Puerto Rico. Privately printed.

Daglish, E. F. (1958). *The Pet-keepers manual.* London. J. M. Dent & Sons.

Davis, J. A. (1966). Notes on 'M'Tundu'. A banded mongoose in the Bronx zoo. *Anim. Kingd.* **69**, 58-59.

Deraniyagala, P. E. P. (1932). Herpetological notes. *Spolia zeylan.* **17**, 44-55.

Deraniyagala, P. E. P. (1951). Some Sinhala combative, field and aquatic sports and games. *Spolia zeylan.* **26**, 179-215.

Dollfus, R. P. (1962). Sur un *Taenia d'Herpestes ichneumon* L. d'Algerie: *Hydatigena laticollis* (Rudolphi 1910), forma *parva* (J. G. Baer, 1925). *Arch. Inst. Pasteur Algér.* **40**, 387-93.

Dotty, R. E. (1945). Rat control on Hawaiian sugar cane plantations. *Hawaii. Plant. Rec.* **49**, 71-239.

Dover, C. (1932). The duration of life of some Indian mammals. *J. Bombay nat. Hist. Soc.* **36**, 244-50.

Drake-Brockman, R. E. (1910). *The mammals of Somaliland.* London. Hurst & Blackett.

*Dubey, J. P., and Pande, B. P. (1963). Observations on the coccidian oocysts from Indian mongoose. *Indian J. Microbiol.* **3**, 49-54.

Dücker, G. (1957). Farb- und Helligkeitssehen und Instinkte bei Viverriden und Feliden. *Zool. Beitr., Berl.* (*N.F.*) **3**, 25-99.

Dücker, G. (1959). Untersuchgen an der Retina einiger Viverriden *Z. Zellforsch.* **51**, 43-49.

Dücker, G. (1960). Beobachtungen über das Paarungverhalten des Ichneumons (*Herpestes ichneumon* L.). *Z. Saügetierk.* **25**, 47-51.

Dücker, G. (1962). Brutpflegeverhalten und Ontogenese des Verhaltens bei Surikaten (*Suricata suricatta* Schreb., Viverridae). *Behaviour* **19**, 305-40.

Dücker, G. (1964). Colour-vision in mammals. *J. Bombay nat. Hist. Soc.* **61**, 572-86.

Dücker, G. (1965). Das Verhalten der Viverriden. *Handb. Zool., Berl.* **8** (38) (10), 1-48.

Durrell, G. (1958). *Encounters with animals.* London. Rupert Hart-Davis.

Du Tertre, R. P. J. B. (1654). *Historie generale des isles de S. Christophe, de la Guadeloupe, de la Martinique, et avetres dans l'Amerique.* Paris.

Edgerton, F. (1965). *The Panchatantra translated from Sanskrit.* London. Allen & Unwin.

Ellerman, J. R., and Morrison-Scott, T. S. C. (1951). *Checklist of Palaearctic and Indian mammals, 1758 to 1946.* London. British Museum (Natural History).

Ellerman, J. R., Morrison-Scott, T. C. S., and Hayman, R. W. (1953). *Southern African mammals 1758-1951: a reclassification.* London. British Museum (Natural History).

Emeneau, M. B. (1940). A classical Indian folk-tale as a reported modern event: the Brahman and the mongoose. *Proc. Am. phil. Soc.* **83**, 503-13.

Eskey, C. R. (1934). Epidemiological study of plague in the Hawaiian Islands. *Publ. Hlth. Bull., Wash.* **213**, 1-70.

Espeut, W. B. (1882). On the acclimatization of the Indian mungoos in Jamaica. *Proc. zool. Soc. Lond.* **1882**, 712-4.

Ewer, R. F. (1963a). The behaviour of the meerkat, *Suricata suricatta* (Schreber). *Z. Tierpsychol.* **20**, 570-607.

Ewer, R. F. (1963b). A note on the suckling behaviour of the Viverrid, *Suricata suricatta* (Schreber). *Anim. Behaviour* **11**, 599-601.

Fantham, H. B. (1923). Some parasitic protozoa found in South Africa. VI. *S. Afr. J. Sci.* **20**, 493-500.

Fayrer, J. (1872). *The Thanophidia of India.* London. J. and A. Churchill.

Feilden, H. W. (1890). Notes on the terrestrial mammals of Barbados. *Zoologist* **14**, 52-55.

Fernando, H. F. (1913). *Herpestes vitticollis*, the stripe-necked mungoose. Sinhalese, Loku Mugatiya. *Ceylon J. Sci.* **8**, 299-300.

Fiedler, W. (1957). Beobachtungen zum Markierungsverhalten einiger Saügetiere. *Z. Saügetierk.* **22**, 57-76.

Fischer, C. E. C. (1921). The habits of the grey mongoose. *J. Bombay nat. Hist. Soc.* **28**, 274.

Fisher, H. I. (1951). The avifauna of Niihau Island, Hawaiian Archipelago. *Condor* **53**, 31-42.

Fitzsimons, F. W. (1919). *The natural history of South Africa* **2**, London. Longmans and Green.

Fleur-de-Lys (1908). The Indian mongoose. *Field* 22nd Feb., p. 320.

Flower, S. S. (1931). Contributions to our knowledge of the duration of life in vertebrate animals. V. Mammals. *Proc. zool. Soc. Lond.* **1931**, 145-234.

Flower, S. S. (1932). Notes on the recent mammals of Egypt, with a list of the species recorded from that Kingdom. *Proc. zool. Soc. Lond.* **1932** (2), 369-450.

Foottit, J. A. W. (1929). Mongoose and snake warfare. *Field* **153**, 828.

Fourie, L. (1936). Field work against plague. *Proc. Transv. Mine med.* **15** (171), 43.

Frechkop, S. (1943). *Exploratie van het Nationaal Albert Park. Mammifères.* Bruxelles.

Fredga, K. (1965a). New sex determining mechanism in a mammal. *Nature, Lond.* **206**, 1176.

Fredga, K. (1965b). A new sex determining mechanism in a mammal. *Hereditas, Lund.* **52**, 411-20.

Frere, A. G. (1929). Breeding habits of the common mongoose (*Herpestes edwardsi*). *J. Bombay nat. Hist. Soc.* **33**, 426-8.

Fuhrmann, O. (1943). Cestodes d'Angola. *Rev. suisse Zool.* **50**, 449-71.

Glickman, S. E., and Sroges, R. W. (1966). Curiosity in zoo animals. *Behaviour* **26**, 151-88.

Gosse, P. H. (1851). *A naturalists' sojourn in Jamaica.* London. Longman, Brown, Green, & Longmans.

Grote, H. (1909). Aufzuchtversuche und Aufzuchten ostafrickanischer Saüger. II. *Zool. Beob.* **50**, 262-5.

Haagner, A. (1920). *South African mammals.* London. Witherby.

Haas, G. E. (1966). Cat flea-mongoose relationships in Hawaii. *J. med. Ent.* **2**, 321-6.

Haldane, J. B. S. (1932). *The causes of evolution.* London.

Hall, E. (1926). My meerkat. *Field* **148**, 395.

Halloran, P. O. (1955). A bibliography of references to diseases of wild mammals and birds. *Am. J. vet. Res.* **16** (2), 1-465.

Hamerton, A. E. (1934). Report on deaths occurring in the society's gardens during the year 1933. *Proc. Zool. Soc. Lond.* **1934**, 389-422.

Hamerton, A. E. (1935). Distribution and comparative morbid anatomy of tuberculosis in captive wild animals. *Brit. J. Tuberc.* **29**, 145-51.

Hamerton, A. E. (1937). Report on the deaths occurring in the society's gardens during the year 1936. *Proc. zool. Soc. Lond.* **107**, 443-74.

Hamerton, A. E. (1941). Report on the deaths occurring in the society's gardens during the years 1939-40. *Proc. zool. Soc. Lond.* (1B) **111**, 151-85.

Harrison, J. L. (1956). Survival rates of Malayan rats. *Bull. Raffles Mus.* **27**, 5-26.

Hayman, R. W. (1940). In Sanderson I. T. The mammals of the North Cameroons Forest Area. Being the results of the Percy Sladen Expedition to the Manfe Division of the British Cameroons. *Trans. zool. Soc. Lond.* **24**, 623-725.

Heck, L. jr. (1956). Beobachtungen an südwestafrikanischen Scharrtieren, *Suricata suricatta hahni* Thomas, 1927. *Saügetierk. Mitt.* **4**, 33-34.

Hediger, H. (1949). Saügetier-Territorien ind ihre Markierung. *Bijdr. Dierk.* **28**, 172-84.

Hediger, H. (1950). *Psychology of animals in zoos and circuses.* London, Butterworth.

Heisch, R. B., Graniger, W. E., Harvey, A. E. C., and Lister G. (1962). Feral aspects of rickettsial infections in Kenya. *Trans. R. Soc. trop. Med. Hyg.* **56**, 272-82.

Heller, E. (1911). New species of rodents and carnivores from equatorial Africa. *Smithson. misc. Coll.* **56** (17), 1-15.

Heller, E. (1937). Ein Ichneumon als Hausgenosse. *Zool. Garten, Lpz.* (*N.F.*) **9**, 222-5.

Henshaw, H. W. (1902). *Birds of the Hawaiian Islands.* Honolulu. Thrum.

Hett, M. L. (1924). On the family Linguatulidae. *Proc. zool. Soc. Lond.* **1924**, 107-59.

Hill, W. C. O. (1956). Longevity in the Ceylon ruddy mongoose *Herpestes smithii zeylanius* Thomas. *J. Bombay nat. Hist. Soc.* **53**, 687-8.

Hinton, H. E. (1957). Biological control of pests. Some considerations. *Sci. Prog., Lond.* **45**, 307-20.

Hollister, N. (1918). East African mammals in the United States National Museum. *Bull. U. S. nat. Mus.* **99**, 1-194.

Hopkins, G. H. E. (1949). The host-associations of the lice of mammals. *Proc. zool. Soc. Lond.* **119**, 387-604.

Howard, L. O. (1897). The spread of land species by the agency of man; with special reference to insects. *Science, N.Y.* (N. S.) **6**, 382-98.

Husson, A. M. (1960). Het voorkomen van de Mungo in Suriname. *Lutra* **2** (1), 12-13.

Hutton, A. F. (1949). Notes on the snakes and mammals of the High Wavy mountains, Madura District. Part II. Mammals. *J. Bombay nat. Hist. Soc.* **48**, 681-94.

Jerdon, T. C. (1867). *The mammalia of India; a natural history of all the animals known to inhabit continental India.* London. Roorkee.

Johri, G. N. (1961). Studies on some cestode parasites. VII. Some old and new cestodes from Indian reptiles in mammals. *Zool. Anz.* **167**, 296-303.

Jsemonger, R. M. (1962). *Snakes of Africa. Southern, Central, and East.* Nelson. Cape Town.

Kinloch, A. P. (1923). The larger mammals of the Nelliampathy Hills. *J. Bombay nat. Hist. Soc.* **29**, 552-4.

Kinloch, B. (1964). *Sauce for the mongoose.* London. Harvill Press.

Kipling, J. L. (1891). *Beast and man in India.* London. Macmillan & Co.

Knowles, R., and Gupta, B. M. D. (1931). A note on two intestinal protozoa of the Indian mongoose. *Indian J. med. Res.* **19**, 175-6.

de Koch, G. (1938). Wild animals as carriers of infection. *S. Afr. med. J.* **12**, 725-30.

Kohls, G. M. (1950). Two new species of ticks from Ceylon (Acarina: Ixodidae). *J. Parasit.* **36**, 319-21.

Koldeway, R. (1914). *The excavations at Babylon* (Translated by A. S. Johns). London. Macmillan & Co.

La Rivers, I. (1948). Some Hawaiian ecological notes. *Wasmann Collect.* **7**, 85-110.

Le Roux, P. L. (1933). On *Tenuostrongylus cynictis*, gen. et sp. n., Trichostrongylid parasitizing the yellow mongoose (*Cynictis penicillata*). *Ann. Mag. nat. Hist.* (10) **11**, 222-8.

Lewis, C. B. (1942). Rats and the mongoose. *Nat. Hist. Notes* **1** (7), 8-9.

Lewis, C. B. (1945). Rats and the mongoose. *Glimpses of Jamaican Natural History*, pp. 15-18. Inst. of Jamaica.

Lewis, C. B. (1953). Rats and the mongoose in Jamaica. *Oryx* **2**, 170-2.

Lewis, E. S. (1940). Mongoose attacking a donkey. *J. Bombay nat. Hist. Soc.* **41**, 893.

Lewis, J. P. (1913). Fight between snake and mongoose. *Ceylon J. Sci.* **9**, 43-44.

Leyhausen, P. (1956). Verhaltensstudien an Katzen. *Z. Tierpsychol.* **2**, 1-120.

Lister, M. D. (1951). Some bird associations of Bengal. *J. Bombay nat. Hist. Soc.* **49**, 695-728.

Lloyd-Jones, W. T. (1953). Habits of the mongoose. *J. Bombay nat. Hist. Soc.* **50**, 397-8.

Lombard, G. L. (1958). The water mongoose *Atilax paludinosus. Fauna & Flora, Transvaal* **9**, 24-27.

Loveridge. A. (1944). Banded mongooses as pets. *Nat. Hist., N. Y.* **53**, 82-83, 96.

Lundholm, B. G. (1955). A taxonomic study of *Cynictis penicillata* (G. Cuvier). *Ann. Transv. Mus.* **22**, 305-19.

Maberly, C. T. A. (1960). *Animals of East Africa.* Cape Town. H. Timmins.

Maingard, J. R. (1954). Sambar deer in Mauritius. *J. Bombay nat. Hist. Soc.* **50**, 648-9.

Marshall, P. M., and Phillips, J. G. (1965). Plan for conserving the wild life of Hong Kong. *Oryx.* **8**, 107-12.

Martin, A. (1891). *Home life on an ostrich farm.* 2nd. ed. George Philip & Son, London.

Matschie, P. (1895). *Die Säugethiere Deutsch-Ost-Afrikas.* Berlin.

Meggitt, F. J. (1924a). On two species of Cestoda from a mongoose. *Parasitology* **16**, 48-54.

Meggitt, F. J. (1924b). *The cestodes of mammals.* Jena. Herman Pohle.

Minette, H. P. (1961). Incidence and serotype of leptospirae isolated from rodents and mongooses on the island of Hawaii. *10th Pacific Sci. Congr. Abstr.* (*Symp. Pap.*) **10**, 420.

Minette, H. P. (1964). Leptospirosis in rodents and mongooses on the island of Hawaii. *Am. J. trop. Med. Hyg.* **13**, 826-32.

Mirza, M. B. (1933). On a new Nemathelminth from *Herpestes mungo.* *Z. Parasitenk.* **6**, 145-6.

Mitton, G. E. (1916). *Lost Cities of Ceylon.* London. John Murray.

Monard, A. (1935). Contribution à la mammologie d'Angola et prodrome d'une faune d'Angola. *Arch. Mus. Bocage* **6**, 1-314.

Monnig, H. O. (1931). Two new nematodes from the suricat (Viverridae). *Rep. vet. Res. S. Afr.* **17**, 277-82.

Monnig, H. O. (1938). A new spirurid nematode from a mongoose. *Livro Jub. Travassos, Rio de Jan.* pp. 333-6.

*Morris, D. (1882). *The mungoose on sugar-estates in the West Indies.* Jamaica. Henderson & Co.

Morris, D. (1961). Eiertikkers en eiergooiers in London en in Amsterdam. *Artis, Amsterdam* **7**, 126-33.

Myers, J. G. (1931a). The present position of the mongoose in the West Indies. *Trop. Agriculture, Trin.* **8** (4), 94-95.

Myers, J. G. (1931b). *A preliminary report on an investigation into the biological control of West Indian insect pests.* E.M.B. **42**. H.M.S.O. London.

Naundorff, E. (1936). Über *Crossarchus obscurus* Fr. Cuv. als Hausgenossen. Carnivoren-Studien. 2. *Kleintier u. Pelz.* **12** (8), 97-102.

*Neitz, W. O. (1937). Rabies in South Africa. *Fmg. in S. Afr.* **12**, 130-3.

Neitz, W. O. (1938). The occurrence of *Nuttallia cynicti* sp. nov. in the yellow mongoose (*Cynictis penicillata*) in South Africa. *Ondersterpoort J. vet. Sci.* **10**, 37-40.

Noguchi, H. (1909). *Snake venoms. An investigation of venomous snakes with special reference to the phenomena of their venoms.* Carnege Inst., Wash., D. C.

Nordmann, A. von (1863). Beobachtungen über einen lebenden *Herpestes mungo* Desmar. *Bull. Soc. Nat. Moscou* **36**, 476-81.

O'Brien. E. (1919). Mongoose (*Mungos mungo*) killing a hedgehog. *J. Bombay nat. Hist. Soc.* **26**, 660.

Odening, K. (1960). Eine neue *Concinum*-Art (Trematoda: Dicrocoeliidae) aus *Herpestes brachyurus* (Carnivora: Viverridae). *Biol. Zbl.* **79**, 513-9.

Oliver, J. A. (1955). Is the mongoose a snake killer? *Nat. Hist., N. Y.* **64**, 426-9.

da Orta, G. (1563). *Coloquios dos simples e drogas de cousas medicinais da India.* (Only the 1913 translation by C. Markham of the 1895 edition by the Conde de Ficalho has been seen).

Ortlepp, R. J. (1938). South African helminths. Part III. Some mammalian and avian cestodes. *Onderstepoort J. vet. Sci.* **11**, 23-50.

Ortlepp, R. J. (1940). South African Helminths. Part VII. Miscellaneous helminths, chiefly cestodes. *Onderstepoort J. vet. Sci.* **14**, 97-110.

Ortlepp, R. J. (1961). On two rictularias and a filarid from South African wild carnivores. *J. Helminth.* (*Leiper Suppl.*), 131-40.

Ortlepp, R. J. (1963). *Pseudandrya mkuzii* sp. nov. (Cestoda: Hymenolepididae) from *Ichneumia albicauda*. *Onderstepoort J. vet. Sci.* **30**, 127-31.

Ortmann, R. (1960). Die Analregion der Saugetiere. *Handb. Zool., Berl.* **8** (26, 3) (7), 1-38.

Palmer, T. S. (1898). The danger of introducing noxious animals and birds. *Yearb. U. S. Dep. Agric.* **1898**, 87 110.

*Pearsall, G. (1947). Notes on some birds of Kauai. *Elepaio. J. Hawaii. Audobon Soc.* **7**, 94-95.

Pearson, O. P., and Baldwin, P. H. (1953). Reproduction and age structure of a mongoose population in Hawaii. *J. Mammal.* **34**, 436-47.

Pemberton, C. E. (1925). The field rat in Hawaii and its control. *Bull. Hawaii. Sug. Ass. ent. Ser.* **17**, 1-46.

Pemberton, C. E. (1933). Some food habits of the mongoose. *Hawaii. Plant. Rec.* **37**, 12-13.

Pergus,— (1852). On the habits of the mongoos (*Herpestes griseus*). *Proc. zool. Soc. Lond.* **1852** (20), 89-90.

Phillips, A. W. A. (1925). A guide to the mammals of Ceylon. Part II. Order Carnivora. *Spolia zeylan.* **13**, 143-93.

Phillips, A. W. A. (1935). *Manual of the mammals of Ceylon.* London. Dulau & Co.

Phillips, A. W. A. (1954). Longevity of the Ceylon ruddy mongoose (*Herpestes smithi zeylanicus*) in captivity. *J. Bombay nat. Hist. Soc.* **52**, 587.

Phillips, A. W. A. (1956). Longevity of the Ceylon ruddy mongoose (*Herpestes smithi zeylanicus*) in captivity. *J. Bombay nat. Hist.* **53**, 464.

Phisalix, C., and Bertrand, G. (1895). Recherches sur l'immunite du herisson contre le venin de vipere. *C. R. Soc. Biol., Paris* (2) **10**, 639-41.

Pimental, D. (1955a). Biology of the Indian mongoose in Puerto Rico. *J. Mammal.* **36**, 62-68.

Pimental, D. (1955b). The control of the mongoose in Puerto Rico. *Am. J. trop. Med. Hyg.* **4**, 147-51.

Pitman, C. R. S. (1938). *A Guide to the snakes of Uganda.* Kampala.

Pitman, C. R. S. (1954). African genets and mongooses. *Zoo Life, Lond.* **9**, 9-12.

Plimmer, H. G. (1912). On the blood-parasites found in animals in the zoological gardens during the four years 1908-1911. *Proc. zool. Soc. Lond.* **1912**, 406-19.

Pocock, R. I. (1916). On the external characters of the mongooses (Mungotidae). *Proc. zool. Soc. Lond.* **1916**, 349-74.

Pocock, R. I. (1919). Classification of the mongooses (Mungotidae). *Ann. Mag. nat. Hist.* (9) **3**, 515-24.

Pocock, R. I. (1941). Mammalia. Vol. II in *Fauna of British India, including Ceylon and Burma.* London. Taylor & Francis.

Powell, J. E. (1913). Notes on the habits of the small Indian mongoose (*Mungos auropunctatus*). *J. Bombay nat. Hist. Soc.* **22**, 620.

Prakash, I., and Sharma, S. C. (1955). Nematodes and hedgehog mortality. *J. Bombay nat. Hist. Soc.* **53**, 123.

Prater, S. H. (1935). The wild animals of the Indian Empire. Part IV. *J. Bombay nat. Hist. Soc.* **38** (Suppl.), 189-215.

Prater, S. H. (1948). *The book of Indian animals.* Bombay.

Preston, F. W. (1950). Mongoose luring guinea fowl. *J. Mammal.* **31**, 194.

Prichard, J. C. (1819). *An analysis of the Egyptian mythology: to which is subjoined a critical examination of the remains of Egyptian chronology.* London. J. & A. Arch.

Rao, H. S. (1957). History of our knowledge of the Indian fauna through the ages. *J. Bombay nat. Hist. Soc.* **54**, 251-80.

Rao, M. A. N. (1939). *Arthrocephalus gambiensis* Ortlepp, 1925. *Indian J. vet. Sci.* **9**, 37-38.

Rensch, B., and Dücker, G. (1959). Die Spiele von Mungo und Ichneumon. *Behaviour* **14**, 185-213.

Rewell, R. (1948). Report of the pathologist for the year 1947. *Proc. zool. Soc. Lond.* **118**, 501-14.

R. L. (1946). Les méfaits de la mangouste. *Nature, Paris* no. 3118, 253-4.

Roberts, A. (1923). The burrowing habits of some South African mammals. *S. Afr. J. nat. Hist.* **4**, 187-208.

Roberts, A. (1951). *The mammals of South Africa.* South Africa. Central News Agency.

Roeder, G. (1936). Das Ichneumon in der ägyptischen Religion und Kunst. *Egypt. Religion* **4**, 1-48.

Roosvelt, T. (1910). *African game trails.* London.

*Roth, V. (1943). *Notes and observations on animal life in British Guiana. A popular guide to Colonial Mammalia.* 3rd ed. Georgetown.

Sandground, J. H. (1937). Three new parasitic nematodes from the Belgian Congo. *Rev. Zool. Bot. afr.* **29**, 230-6.

Schaffer, J. (1940). *Die Hautdrüsenorgane der Saugetiere.* Berlin. Urban & Schwarzenberg.

Schmidt, K. P. (1928). Amphibians and land reptiles of Porto Rico, with a list of those reported from the Virgin Islands. In *Scientific survey of Porto Rico and the Virgin Islands* **10** (1), 1-160. N. Y. Acad Sci.

*Schwartz, C. W., and Schwartz, E. R. (1949). *The game birds in Hawaii.* Honolulu. Board of Agriculture and Forestry.

Schwartz, C. W., and Schwartz, E. R. (1950). The California quail in Hawaii. *Auk* **67**, 1-38.

Schwartz, C. W., and Schwartz, E. R. (1951). A survey of the lace-necked dove in Hawaii. *Pacif. Sci.* **5**, 90-107.

Schwarz, E. (1935). On a new mongoose from the Cameroons. *Ann. Mag. nat. Hist.* (10) **15**, 300-1.

*Schwarz, E. (1943). Notes on commensal rats. *Pests* **11**, 6.

Schwarz, E. (1947). Colour mutants of the Malay short-tailed mongoose, *Herpestes brachyurus* Gray. *Proc. zool. Soc. Lond.* **117**, 79-80.

Sclater, W. L. (1900). *Mammals of South Africa. I. Primates, Carnivora and Ungulata.* London. Porter.

Seaman, G. A. (1952). The mongoose and Caribbean wildlife. *Trans. 17th N. Am. Wild Life Conf.* **17**, 188-97.

Seaman, G. A., and Randall, J. E. (1962). The mongoose as a predator in the Virgin Islands. *J. Mammal.* **43**, 544-6.

Shortridge, G. C. (1934). *The mammals of South West Africa. A biological account of the forms occurring in that region.* **1**. London. W. Heinemann.

Simpson, C. D. (1964). Notes on the banded mongoose, *Mungos mungo* (Gmelin). *Arnoldia (Rhodesia)* **1**, (19), 1-8.

Simpson, C. D. (1966). The banded mongoose. *Anim. Kingd.* **69**, 52-57.

Singh, K. G. (1956). Game preservation in Jammu and Kashmir State. *J. Bombay nat. Hist. Soc.* **53**, 646-50.

*Smith, J. D., and Woodworth, J. R. (1951). A study of the pheasant, California quail and lace-necked dove in Hawaii. *Fish & Game Div. Special Bull.* **3** (Bd. Agric. & For., Honolulu).

Smith, J. H. (1914). Mongoose v. cobra. *J. Bombay nat. Hist. Soc.* **22**, 789.

Snyder, D. P. (1956). Survival rates, longevity, and population fluctuations in the white-footed mouse, *Peromyscus leucopus*, in Southeastern Michigan. *Misc. Publ. Zool. Univ. Mich.* **95**, 1-33.

Snyman, P. S. (1940). The study and control of vectors of rabies in South Africa. *Onderstepoort J. vet. Sci.* **15**, 9-140.

Spasskii, A. H. (1951). *Anoplocephalate tapeworms of domestic and wild animals.* Moscow. Academy of Sciences, USSR.

Spencer, H. J. (1950). Mongoose control research project. *Fish. Bull. U. S.* 1-9.

Spurway, H. (1953). The escape drive in domestic cats and the dog and cat relationship. *Behaviour* **5**, 81-84.

Steinbacher, G. (1939). Nuesse oeffnender Sumpfichneumon. *Zool. Garten, Lpz.* (*N.F.*) **10**, 228-9.

Steinbacher, G. (1951). Nüsse öffnender Sumpfichneumon. *Zool. Garten, Lpz.* (*N.F.*) **18**, 58.

Sterndale, R. A. (1884). *Natural history of the Mammalia of India and Ceylon.* London. Thacker, Spink, & Co.

Stevenson-Hamilton, J. (1947). *Wild Life in South Africa.* London. Cassell & Co.

Stoner, C. R. (1944). Observations on the elephant and other mammals in the Anamalai Hills of Cochin. *J. Bombay nat. Hist. Soc.* **44**, 588-92.

Takashima, H. (1954). Considerations on the change of animal life in Japan. II. *Misc. Rep. Yamashina Inst. Orn. Zool.* **4**, 146-55. (In Japanese, French summary.)

Taylor, K. D. (1965). *The rat and mongoose problem in Grenada.* London Min. Agric. Food & Fisheries (internal report).

Taylor, S., and Webb, C. S. (1955). Breeding dwarf mongooses. *Zoo Life, Lond.* **10**, 70-72.

Tembrock, G. (1963). Acoustic behaviour of mammals. In *Acoustic behaviour of animals*, pp. 751-86. Ed. R.-G. Busnell. Amsterdam.

Thomas, A. D., and Neitz, W. O. (1933). The importance of disease in wild animals. *S. Afr. J. Sci.* **30**, 419-25.

Thompson, G. B. (1950). Ticks of Jamaica, B. W. I.-Records and notes (including a summary of the distribution of the West Indian species). *Ann. Mag. nat. Hist.* (12) **3**, 220-9.

Tierkel, E. S., Arbona, G., Rivera, A., and de Juan, A. (1952). Mongoose rabies in Puerto Rico. *Public Hlth Rep., Wash.* **67**, 274-8.

Urich, F. W. (1914). The mongoose in Trinidad and methods of destroying it. *Circ. Dep. Agric. Trin. Tob.* **12**, 1-16.

Urich, F. W. (1931). The mongoose in Trinidad. *Trop. Agriculture, Trin.* **8** (4), 95-97.

de Vos, A., and Manville, R. H. (1956). Introduced mammals and their influence on native biota. *Zoologica, N. Y.* **41**, 163-94.

Vossler, J. (1907). Aus dem Leben ostafrikanischen Säuger. *Zool. Beob.* **48**, 164-79; 193-206; 225-41.

Walker, E. P. (1942). Care of captive animals. *Ann. Rep. Smithson. Inst.* **1941**, 305-66.

Walker, E. P. (1964). *Mammals of the world.* **2**. Baltimore. The Johns Hopkins Press.

Walker, L. W. (1945). The Hawaiian mongoose—friend or foe. *Nat. Hist. N. Y.* **54**, 396-400.

Walker, L. W. (1948). Citizen mongoose. *Audobon Mag.* **50**, 80-85.

Webb-Peploe, C. G. (1947). Field notes on the mammals of South Tinnevelly, South India. *J. Bombay nat. Hist. Soc.* **46**, 629-44.

Weir, J. M., and Horsfall, F. L. (1940). The recovery from patients with acute pneumonitis of a virus causing pneumonia in the mongoose. *J. exp. Med.* **72**, 595-610.

Westermann, J. H. (1953). Nature preservation in the Caribbean. A review of literature on the destruction and preservation of flora and fauna in the Caribbean area. *Publ. Found. Sci. Res. Surinam & Netherlands Antilles* **9**, 1-106.

Wilkinson, J. G. (1878). *The manners and customs of the ancient Egyptians.* **3**. London. John Murray.

Williams, C. B. (1918). Mongoose. The food habits of the mongoose in Trinidad. *Bull. Dep. Agric. Trin. Tob.* **17**, 167-86.

Wolcott, G. N. (1924). The food of Porto Rican lizards. *J. Dep. Agric. P. R.* **7**, 5-37.

Wolcott, G. N. (1953). Food of mongoose (*Herpestes javanicus auropunctatus* Hodgson) in St Croix and Puerto Rico. *J. Agric. Univ. P. R.* **37**, 241-7.

Wroughton, R. C. (1915). Bombay Natural History Society's mammal survey of India, Burma, and Ceylon. *J. Bombay nat. Hist. Soc.* **24**, 79-110.

Index

All references to mammals (except mongooses), birds, lizards, snakes, and insects and other arthropods are listed under one or other of these headings. Pages on which line drawings occur are in heavy type.